GET LUCKY

GET LUCKY

The Memoirs of Lord Lucan

edited by Dickon Whitfield

B⬛XTREE

First published in Great Britain in 1995 by Boxtree Limited,
Broadwall House, 21 Broadwall, London SW1 9PL

10 9 8 7 6 5 4 3 21

ISBN: 0 7522 0745 8

A CIP catalogue entry for this book is available from the British
Library.

Printed and bound in Great Britain by
Butler & Tanner Ltd, Frome and London

Contents

1. Lucky Strike

Gamblers are different. Spiritually, morally, philosophically, but above all, financially. Skint. That's usually how we are. And when you're skint you're a bloody fool on the lookout for a bigger fool, which is how I met Carlos.

I was at the Clermont, the Mayfair gaming club that was something of a home-from-home for me in those days some two decades ago. The evening began like so many others. The usual sort of mid-week crowd, mostly regulars with a dash of unfamiliar faces. After dinner – lamb cutlets, my habitual fodder (grilled in winter, *en gelée* in summer) – I looked for Gussie and Boy – we'd arranged to play together. But they were damned late, so I went ahead and sat down at a table. By the time they showed their noses all the seats were bagged. Since I'd got the measure of the other players and was happily quids-in, I stayed put pro tem and went on playing.

Later when I wandered over, the game Gussie and Boy had joined was in full swing so I just stood and watched. Next to Boy sat a stranger, a moon- faced, foreign-looking young fellow with a wispy moustache wearing a trendy jacket and a loud tie. A bounder, if ever I'd seen one. But it wasn't his unprepossessing appearance that was memorable, it was his poker. Diabolical. A complete duffer, even worse than old Squiffy Marchmain. Just the few hands I saw him play must have set him back a good £3,000. A Heaven-sent candidate, if ever I saw one, for one of our afternoon private parties.

Later on we met in the bar, and I bought us drinks – a Scotch for him, a vodka martini for me. He called himself

Carlos Sanchez and said he was from Venezuela. It transpired that Boy and he had been on the same table at a ball at the Dorchester a few nights before. Their conversation had turned to cards and Boy had invited him along to the Clermont. He worked, so he said, in the import-export business, shipping goods between Europe and Latin America. He told me that he was living with his mother in Bayswater and even showed me a photograph of her that he carried in his wallet. A nice touch, I later realised, for allaying suspicion.

'Just call me Johnny,' I said as I suggested he might have better luck with the cards at one of our select little gatherings. He thanked me warmly and I think he was genuinely pleased at the invitation. He explained that unfortunately he was being transferred to Paris and would be unable to take up my offer. But should I ever find myself at a loose end in the French capital and fancying a game of poker I should give him a call. He gave me his card, which I put in my wallet for sake-keeping. In my line of biz it wasn't often that one met a turkey who invited you round for Christmas dinner.

★★★

I'm not going to reveal any details of my actions immediately after the terrible events of that November night in 1974 that branded me a murderer. To do so could only harm the loyal friends who looked after me in my darkest hour and spirited me away from almost certain imprisonment for a crime of which I am innocent.

It was time to lie doggo. With the help of a friend, Jennifer – not her real name – I found myself staying as a paying-guest in a secluded villa at Cap Ferrat. My hosts – let's call them Cedric and Agatha – were elderly English gentlefolk of the old school. Cedric was a retired stockbroker who'd seen active service in Special Operations during the war and was still addressed as Major. He looked the part too, with his little white toothbrush moustache and a military bearing. His passion was his pocket handkerchief-sized garden, where he pottered around for much of the day. Agatha had a warm, maternal manner, though like so many women of the English shires she had the mettle of a tigress if the occasion demanded.

Her interests were astrology and the spirit world, trotting over to Villefranche-sur-Mer a couple of afternoons a week to participate in ouija board sessions in the apartment of a Madame Velasquez.

Cedric and Agatha had been living on the Riviera for about a decade. Sensibly, not wanting to be fleeced of their savings by the socialists, they'd done a bunk from Britain when the Labour lot won in 1964. But now, explained Jennifer, whose family had been their neighbours in Camberley back in the old days, money was a bit tight and taking in occasional paying guests helped make ends meet.

Jennifer came round most afternoons for a cup of tea and a few hands of Racing Demon or Pontoon in my small room, the bed serving as our card-table. She was a spirited filly, aged about 25, with a healthy hockey-sticks complexion, a comely Gloucestershire figure and a genial nature. She had pretty cornflower-coloured eyes and blonde shoulder-length hair, usually held back with an Alice band. She'd been working during the summer at the harbour at St Jean in a yacht-hire bureau and had stayed on after the season. I knew her through mutual friends at home, a shared enthusiasm for boats forging a bond between us. I had taken her out on the town a couple of times and we'd had quite a hoot, but there was no boudoir hanky-panky. We were simply muckers. Or so I thought.

Jennifer introduced me to Cedric and Agatha as a novelist who was working on a book. It was the perfect cover-story, explaining why I spent most of the day in my room with the door closed and never set foot outside the house. In fact, I whiled away the hours working my way through the anthology of Wodehouse stories, a pile of old Giles cartoon annuals and a volume borrowed from my hosts' bookshelf, David Niven's amusing autobiography *The Moon's A Balloon*. I also started scribbling myself, at first to lend authenticity to my assumed identity but soon because I enjoyed it. The diary I started writing then, and have kept ever since, is the basis for these memoirs.

The alias of a writer provided me with a licence for eccentric behaviour, even explaining the drastic change in my appearance that occurred during the weeks I spent with Cedric and Agatha. On arrival I was sensibly attired in a blazer, a light blue polo-neck shirt, grey flannel trousers and a pair of Gucci shoes. Jennifer said that my clothes were a bit of a giveaway and insisted on a change. She took my measurements and beetled-off to Monte Carlo, returning with a pile of the most gopping togs I'd ever seen – a pair of flared blue-jeans, a denim jacket, a pink T-shirt, a red gypsy-like neckerchief, and some white sneakers. And there was worse to come.

Right at the start of my travails I'd shaved off my moustache to disguise myself, but that wasn't enough for Jennifer. At her prompting I began to grow long side-whiskers, which she told me were *branché*, as they say over there, amongst the Riviera fast-set. Then one evening she appeared with a plastic carrier bag containing various potions that she applied to my hair. The results were remarkable. Gone were my dark, slick looks. Now my head was covered by straw-coloured strands that sprouted vertically from my scalp. I looked like an albino gollywog. Jennifer said the style was called an 'Afro' and matched my new clothes, completing my new fashionable image. 'Darling you look frightfully trendy,' she giggled gleefully. 'No-one would ever dream that you were really that crusty, pompous, old stick-in-the-mud, Lucky Lucan.'

I studied myself in the mirror. The transformation was certainly remarkable. I no longer looked remotely respectable, let alone like a peer of the realm. I looked a complete ponce – a damn fine disguise.

Jennifer drove me round to the railway station where they had one of those self-service machines for passport photos. That evening, some deft work with a razor blade, a can of lighter fluid and a Bic biro fixed the flimsy British Visitor's visa, on which I was travelling, to fit the new me. Good-bye Richard John Bingham, ninth Earl Lucan of Castlebar. Hello plain John Smith.

★★★

I followed the great Lord Lucan hunt through the pages of the *Daily Mail*, which was delivered to the villa daily at about 4 o'clock. I was being spotted all over the place: in Britain; in South Africa; in Brazil; and even *en route* for Haiti with £100,000 in my pocket. If only! In fact, I was seriously pushed and the dosh situation was starting to weigh on my mind.

The British police were reported to have conducted inch-by-inch searches of a dozen country houses, two stately homes and had alerted every gaming club world-wide to be on the lookout. Reading that, I determined never to cross the threshold of a casino again. A resolution I have kept to this day.

The paper was full of stories of policemen with tracker-dogs combing the Sussex downs and frogmen plumbing the murky depths of Newhaven harbour. Detectives interviewed 150 of my friends – a chat with the Rozzers must have given old Squiffy Marchmain the raving abdabs – and a posse of them went off on a wild goose chase to Normandy. But despite making a perfect nuisance of themselves, the 40-

strong murder squad wasn't getting anywhere. Relations between the police and the 'toffs', as they were quoted as referring to my chums, soon became strained and the boys-in-blue began to get impatient to get back to the more congenial pastime of chasing the criminal class. 'For one thing,' one of them told the press, 'when you are dealing with villains, you at least know where to find them.'

Lunch I took by myself in my room, but in the evening I joined Cedric and Agatha for dinner. We soon developed a routine whereby they expressed a polite interest in the progress of my writing and I responded with a few authorish-sounding remarks. I had no idea what I was talking about, I just parroted what Jennifer had told me to say about the 'dilemmas of characterisation' and the 'problems of viewpoint'. We then moved on to more interesting matters, mostly the news of the day from home and abroad. And what a dismal and depressing catalogue of events. The new Labour government had imposed some swingeing taxes to pay for its socialist antics and its sell-out to the trade union bully-boys. The IRA murdered a score of innocents in a Birmingham pub. Arab terrorists hi-jacked a plane and held the passengers hostage in Tunis. Cedric expressed the view that it was time to bring back hanging for the perpetrators of such deeds. I obligingly agreed, though wondering what Gussie and Boy would say if they heard me endorsing such namby-pamby liberal sentiments. The full rigours of a medieval torture chamber was more like their idea of punishment to fit the crimes.

***

The local ex-pats were a clubbable lot. Drinks parties were two-a-penny, the pretexts being distinctly ingenious. I recall celebrating the anniversary of the opening of Piccadilly Circus underground station, the departure of Sir Francis Drake on his voyage round the world, and the battle of

Magersfontein. Nobody was quite sure when or where the battle of Magersfontein took place, or even who we'd been fighting, but that didn't mar the proceedings. People were forever dropping in for a cup of tea, or something stronger. I went to ground while visitors were about, staying in my room with the door shut and locked. But one day, I heard a voice that drew me from my den like a siren's singing. It belonged to a scrawny, dapper, distinguished-looking man with a pencil-line military moustache. I recognised him immediately.

'Ah,' exclaimed Cedric, spying me peeping into the corridor, 'come and meet David Niven, a neighbour and a good friend. David, this is our house guest, Johnny Smith. He's writing a novel.'

'You've picked a good spot for it,' said Niven genially, as we pressed palms. 'Somerset Maughan did all his scribbling round the corner at the Villa Mauresque, and P.G. Wodehouse wrote *Thank You, Jeeves* just down the road. Must be something in the air.'

'I'm a great admirer of Wodehouse's work,' I said, trying to sound authorish.

'But David, you too are a writer,' Agatha chipped in.

'Actually, your book is by my bedside at the moment,' I ventured. 'Drollest stuff I've read for years.'

'Thank you,' said Niven with a slight shrug of the shoulders and the most modest of smiles. 'Tell me about your own writing, Mr Smith.'

'Errr, it's . . . I mean . . . Well, there's . . .,' I spluttered. 'Oh gosh, it's sort of about a chap who's on the run in the Cote d'Azur.'

'A thriller eh?' said Niven, interestedly, arching his eyebrows. 'Is the fugitive an English gentleman, by any chance?'

'Yes, he is, actually.'

'I thought he might be. Is he a dashing, derring-do sort of chap?'

'Oh, rather.'

'A mature man with uncommonly fine features, particularly his moustache?'

'Exactly so.'

'And a sensitive nature, despite being something of a rogue. A bit of a romantic, in fact.'

'That's right'

'I like the sound of him. Just the sort of part I'm looking for. Have you done any film writing?'

'No, no. I'm strictly a prose writer,' I replied, deciding that my career as a writer had made quite enough progress for one afternoon.

Niven looked a little disappointed.

'I say,' he said. 'I'm on my way to do some filming right now. It's a commercial to sell whisky to the Japanese. We're shooting in the garden of a villa on the other side of the Cap. Come along, and have a look. It should be quite a lot of fun.'

I was flabbergasted. David Niven, one of my favourite actors, was inviting me to toddle along to watch him at work. Of course I accepted.

A chauffeur-driven car was waiting outside to take us to the shoot. As we drove, David, as he insisted I call him, told me about Raffles, the legendary English gentleman thief who he had in mind as the proto-type for the hero of my story. He was entirely gone on the idea of portraying him on screen. Not that I'd uttered a word about robbing hotel safes or seducing countesses at the gaming tables and stealing their diamond tiaras. Mind you, given the parlous state of my finances they were interesting suggestions. And then we pulled into a drive and car and conversation came to a halt outside a large white villa.

There was mayhem in the garden. Half-a-dozen chimpanzees, two dressed as bride and groom and the rest in formal morning wear or wide-brimmed hats and cocktail dresses, were having a party. Niven explained that he played the part of an English butler who had a trying time serving tea to the scampish blighters and found solace in a glass of Scotch. Sure it was childish and slap-stick. That was just the way the Japanese liked their commercials.

My view of the proceedings was obscured by a crowd of camera operators, lighting technicians, girls with clip-boards, and assorted hangers-on. To see better, I built a platform out of a couple of empty wooden crates and stepped up on top. It was rollickingly funny to see David attempting to maintain a stiff-upper-lip while serving tea to the unruly apes. In fact, I laughed so much that I lost my balance, setting in train an unfortunate sequence of events.

As the boxes tipped forward I jumped down to avoid falling, landing on the end of a plank left behind by the set builders. Perched on the other end was a tin of paint that flew through the air, striking me on the shoulder and splattering me with red splotches. I stumbled backwards, tripping over a camera cable and landing on the wheeled trolley that was used for tracking shots. The force of the impact must have released the brake, since it started moving down the slope that led to the swimming pool. I struggled to my feet in order to jump off, but was unable to do so before it hit the pool-side stone parapet and came to an abrupt halt. I flew into the air, my flight-path tracing a perfect parabola, and landed in the pool with an enormous splash. Being mid-winter, the water was freezing cold and filthy with algae and dead leaves. I must have looked like the Creature from the Black Lagoon, as I hoisted myself back on to *terra firma*.

Much to my surprise my acrobatics received a rave reception, even the monkeys joining in the applause. There was general agreement that it was the best piece of slap-stick anyone had seen for ages, the names of Buster Keaton and Charlie Chaplin were bandied about. Amongst the French,

Monsieur Hulot was the name on everyones' lips, and David Niven muttered something about Norman Wisdom, that I took at the time to be a compliment. The director of the commercial, a real four-letter man called Klaus, suggested I should join the chimps at the tea table, declaring that I had the makings of a comedy mega-star in Japan.

Declining his offer, I made my way home in my bedraggled state. Immediately I developed a dreadful cold that put me in bed for several days. Jennifer came round and remonstrated with me for going open-air swimming at such a time of year. She declared that I needed properly looking-after, and announced that was just what she would do from now on.

***

Even more disturbing, was the close interest taken by Agatha in the disappearance of Lord Lucan, a subject that came up in conversation at the dinner table almost nightly. She was convinced that he had been framed by Prime Minister Harold Wilson's shady henchmen as part of a socialist plot to discredit the aristocracy and abolish the monarchy. Apparently Lucan had revealed this to her himself during one of Madame Velasquez's ouija board sessions. I pointed out that to communicate through the ouija board, Lucan would have had to have passed over to the "other side". 'Oh yes,' she replied, 'he's dead all right. Dead as a Dodo. Done in by Wilson's wide-boys and dumped overboard in the English Channel, the body weighed-down by copies of *Das Kapital*.' We all nodded sagely at this intelligence.

Mine wasn't the only disappearance in the press. A few days after my arrival at Cap Ferrat it was reported that John Stonehouse, Labour MP and former Postmaster General, had vanished from a beach in Miami leaving behind a pile of clothes. Apparently Stonehouse was an avid swimmer and at first it was assumed that he had drowned, being carried away by the strong tides. Then strange stories started to circulate. It was revealed that his car had recently been blown-up in the car park at Heathrow Airport. There were suggestions that the bombing of an Army catering unit near his home was a bungled attempt on his life. This seemed far-fetched. After all, everyone who'd been in the forces had a powerful grievance against the Catering Corps. One of Stonehouse's aids suggested that he might have been bumped-off by the Mob and the FBI seized a large slab of concrete on suspicion that it was a Mafia-style 'concrete overcoat'. A Czech defector called Joseph Frolick, an apt-sounding surname, denounced Stonehouse as a Soviet agent. Then there were guarded references to some dubious goings-on in his business affairs and suggestions that he might have legged-it to avoid his creditors. By now I was thoroughly bewildered. But not Cedric. He said it was par for the course for socialist ministers to be gangsters, Russian spies and fraudsters. 'Probably promiscuous as a goat too,' he exclaimed with remarkable foresight.

Also much in the news was Lieutenant-Colonel John Brooks, a 64 year old, bowler-hatted and ostensibly straight up-and-down London solicitor, former mayor of Kensington and Chelsea and a keen huntsman. Another of his pastimes was luring 'good-natured young ladies', as he called them, on to his motor boat on the Thames, where he removed their knickers and spanked their bare bottoms. He then anointed their posteriors with whisky. His activities were exposed by *The Sunday People*, who commented that he was a menace to young women. Brooks sued for libel in the High Court, ensuring that the whole world learned about his antics.

Curiouser and curiouser. But not for Agatha. She saw a pattern in the Lucan, Stonehouse and Brooks episodes. For a start, they were all called John. But more tellingly, they had all served in the armed forces, risking their lives for King and country like her own dear Cedric. To her it was clear as a bell what was really afoot. Harold Wilson and his jack-booted lackeys were attempting to discredit the military, the legal profession and Parliament, the very bastions of the British way of life. This was going a bit far. I'd never heard of Wilson's entourage wearing jack-boots, but I kept my peace so as not to upset our domestic harmony. When Brooks won his case, being awarded a half-penny damages, Agatha saw it as a victory against the dark forces and that evening we broke open the Bollinger.

Jennifer also took a keen interest in the Colonel Brooks case, her voice taking on a tremulous tone and her eyes twinkling whenever the subject was mentioned. One afternoon, when Cedric was tending his garden and Agatha was chez Madame Velasquez, we were playing a hand of Hearts in my room when she asked my opinion of Tom Jones. Thinking she was referring to the singer of the ballad *The Green Green Grass of Home*, one of my favourites, I expressed great admiration. But, as it soon became clear, the Tom Jones she had in mind was the squire of that name in the novel by Henry Fielding, whose rumbustious, romp-in-the-hay, bottom-slapping behaviour had been referred to in court as Brooks' role-model.

Jennifer beamed at my words, rose to her feet, hoisted her dirndl up around her head and flung herself on to the bed face down, revealing a bare bottom. The cards went flying.

'Spank me. Beat me,' she cried.

'I say, steady on, old sausage,' I bleated, picking up the cards and trying to reconstruct our hands. I noticed, as I'd suspected, that she was holding the Queen of Spades.

'Get on with it,' commanded Jennifer, in the forthright manner of Fielding's heroines.

I stared at the swathe of pink flesh and my spirits plummeted. Yes, alright, I wasn't in jail, but I was just as much a prisoner. I was at Jennifer's mercy. Her plaything. Today spanking was her whim. Tomorrow, Lord knows what it might be. As my hand swished down on the starkers posterior, I decided that it was time to move on. But to get really away, a long way away, I needed money, and lots of it – enough to buy a proper passport and a long-haul air ticket. And then I remembered Carlos's card; more importantly, I remembered just how bad at poker he'd been.

***

I called him that very afternoon. A girl answered the 'phone. She said she would take a message and he'd call back. I told her that my name was Johnny – John Smith – and that I'd met Carlos in London and he'd suggested we should get together for a game of poker if I was visiting Paris. I'd be there in a couple of days and would like to take up the invitation.

Carlos called back about an hour later. He sounded surprised to hear from me and it was pretty clear that he had no idea who I was. Nevertheless, he said that he'd be delighted to see me and we arranged a meeting a few days hence. He was full of curiosity about what I was up to in France and by persistent questioning managed to extract from me that I was staying at Cap Ferrat and would be taking the night train from Nice to Paris the day after tomorrow. At the time I thought nothing of volunteering the information. Looking back from the vantage point of twenty one years of life as a fugitive, I marvel at my naiveté.

***

On the evening of my departure for Paris, Jennifer called to collect me in her red Renault 4. There was a touching farewell with my hosts who said that they were very sorry to see me go and hoped that I'd come again if I found myself in that part of the world. Cedric asked me to send them a copy of the book and I promised to do so. Here it is, better late than never, as the bard might have put it.

I asked Agatha if she'd had any more messages from Lord Lucan and she said yes, she'd been speaking to him that very afternoon.

'He told me what he misses most is lamb cutlets. You know, he had lamb cutlets for lunch and dinner every single day of his life. It said so in the newspaper. Remarkably single-minded, don't you think? Anyway, apparently they don't have lamb cutlets on the "other side".'

Agatha's words had a singular effect on me. My whole being was overcome with nostalgia – for my friends and the club. Tears welled up into my eyes. There was pain in my soul. An aching in my stomach. At that moment, I would have done anything for a lamb cutlet. Even Morris dancing.

'Mind you,' Cedric chipped in, 'with the Labour Party running the economy, pretty soon the British won't have anything to eat on this side either.'

***

Jennifer accompanied me into the railway station and helped me find the carriage with the compartment I had reserved. She blubbed a bit as we stood on the bleak windy platform saying good-bye.

'Chin up, old sausage,' I said affectionately and gave her a peck on the cheek and a pat on the bottom. That seemed to do the trick, the tears giving way to a brave-faced smile. I mounted the steps and climbed aboard the train, dumping my bag in my compartment. Returning to the corridor, I slid open one of the windows and leaned out.

'Now just remember,' said Jennifer sternly, 'don't talk to strangers and remember to write.' It was just like setting off for boarding school.

'See you next week,' I said cheerily and gave a reassuring

grin. But, in fact, I had no intention at all of returning to the Riviera for the foreseeable future.

We chatted away for several minutes, just like in *Brief Encounter*, until the train began to pull out of the station. But she didn't have my undivided attention, since I was somewhat distracted by the figure of a tall, slender, dark-haired young woman in a long mink coat who was slowly making her way along the corridor, reading the names on the reservation slips that were posted outside each compartment. When she reached my compartment she seemed to pause, as if my name had some special significance. But I was mistaken, for she resumed her quest and disappeared into the next carriage.

As the train was almost empty, I was the sole occupant of the First Class Sleeper. I changed into my maroon and navy Guards-stripe pyjamas and settled into the lower bunk. The sheets were crisply pressed and rustled deliciously as I slipped between them. The heating was going full tilt and soon the compartment was luxuriantly snug. The gentle swaying of the train and its rhythmic rumblings were pleasantly soothing. Opening the Dick Francis Jennifer had given me for the journey, I began to read.

The door swished open. I looked up. The girl in the mink slid into the compartment. She was carrying a small overnight bag which she placed on the upper bunk. She smiled at me. Unbuttoning the fur coat, she slipped it off her shoulders. Chanel No. 5 wafted around the compartment on the eddies of warm air. She was wearing crimson satin hot-pants and a tight low-cut black top that hugged and sculpted her full breasts. Stepping forward she put the coat up with her bag, my field of vision being entirely taken up by the pair of long legs in black fishnet tights surmounted by skin-tight shiny hot-pants. Was it really possible that this stranger, with all the qualifications of a *Playboy Magazine* centre-fold model, had been billeted in my compartment? Surely there had been a mistake?

'*Bon soir*, my name is Marie,' she said in a sexy, breathy voice, with an accent as French as frogs legs, as she sat down on the side of my bed. 'I'm a Virgo.'

'I'm John. I'm . . . err . . . English. Very pleased to meet you,' I replied falteringly. 'I say, do you think there's been some sort of a mix-up? I mean . . .'

But Marie wasn't listening. She pouted smoulderingly and handed me a chilled bottle of champagne, which she must have extracted from her bag. In her other hand were two plastic cups. Now over the years, I've opened more bottles of bubbly than I've had hot dinners, lamb cutlets or any other sort, but that night I was all thumbs and I made a dreadful bish of the business. The cork shot out, ricocheting round the compartment, and wine gushed from the neck drenching my hands and pyjamas. Marie leaned forward. She licked the droplets from my fingers, one by one, and ran her tongue down my wrists. She looked up and gazed into my eyes. She was close, so close I could feel the warmth of her breath.

'John,' she said, 'in France they say that all Englishmen are homosexuals. Is this true?'

'That's a stinking slander,' I spluttered. 'It's an outrage.'

'So you are not a homosexual?'

'No, certainly not.'

'That is good,' she said. She sat up and slowly peeled off the black blouse. She arched forward, her breasts brushing my chest. Our mouths met. We kissed, hungrily, voraciously.

'Move over, John,' she whispered in my ear. Momentarily, I wondered what on earth I was doing. But wasn't the reputation of English manhood at stake? I pushed myself up against the wall and she slithered into the bed like a serpent. Our bodies entwined . . .

★★★

'Why do you go to Paris?' asked Marie later, as we lounged on the bed drinking champagne and the train sped north through the night, across the maquis towards Avignon.

'To do some research.'

'What do you research?'

'A story. I am a writer.'

'*C'est vrai?*' she exclaimed, sounding very surprised. 'Are you famous?'

'No, I'm afraid not. But I make enough to get by.'

'What is the story about?'

'It's a love story, of course. That's why I'm setting it in Paris. As they say "Paris loves lovers".'

'You have friends at Paris?'

'I know an old school friend who lives there.'

'Which school is that?'

I was suddenly suspicious. Why such a question? What possible interest could it be to her? Could it be that I was under the covers with an undercover *gendarme*?

'Oh you wouldn't have heard of it,' I replied evasively, since even in France they probably knew about Eton.

'Was it one of those English schools where they hit you with sticks?'

'Yes, I suppose it was.'

'And you enjoyed that?'

'Oh, wacking isn't for pleasure. It's character building.'

'But your Colonel Brooks . . .'

'A good example. Flogging is a tradition aboard British boats. How do you think we won the battle of Trafalgar?' I knew I was talking balderdash, but I was becoming irritated by her aspersions about my countrymen. I soothed myself with another slug of champagne.

Marie looked puzzled, but she let the subject drop and resumed her interrogation.

'You went to the university?'

'Yes, in London.' I lied, deciding to muddy the water with misinformation.

'And your *service militaire*?' she continued relentlessly. Marie would have had a shining career in the Gestapo.

'In the Royal Air Force,' I said. That seemed as distant from the Coldstream Guards as you could get.

'Most writers are *gauchistes*. You are of the left?'

'Sure,' I said, 'I'm Harold Wilson's biggest fan.' I yawned. The sex, the champagne, the lulling rhythm of the *chemin de fer* and all those questions had sapped my strength. It was shut-eye time.

★★★

I was awoken by the crash of breaking glass. The empty champagne bottle had rolled across the floor of the compartment and smashed against the foot of my bunk bed.

Marie was gone. I lay there thinking about her and about the whole strange episode. I realised my suspicion that she was from the police was absurd. A thief was much more likely.

I leapt up. Tip-toeing between the shards of glass I reached my jacket hanging on the back of the door and checked the pockets. But my money and my documents were still there. So what did she want? Maybe it really was my body. They were a rum bunch, these foreigners.

★★★

The Gare de Lyon was bustling with early morning rush-hour traffic. I took the Metro to the Boulevard St Michel in the teeming Latin Quarter. Walking down one of the side streets, I soon found a cheap Bohemian hotel of the sort I was looking for. I was a filthy fleapit, but I knew that if I paid cash in advance there wouldn't be any bother about identity papers. I took a few hours' kip and then in the early afternoon I went off in search of one of the many little cinemas that pepper the neighbourhood. By an extraordinary coincidence, the first one I came upon was showing the film *Tom Jones*. I bought a ticket and went in. What an exhausting way of life it portrayed, and how it brought home to me just how timely my escape from Jennifer had been.

I supped on *cotelettes d'agneau* in a cheap neighbourhood restaurant for a few francs. Then, at last, it was time to call on Carlos and make some boodle.

I rang the bell of the flat in the Rue Toullier, just round the corner from the Sorbonne. Imagine my astonishment and delight when Marie, the girl on the train, opened the door. I expressed amazement at this bizarre coincidence, but she just shrugged and beckoned me inside.

Carlos greeted me cordially and almost instantly I had a large brandy and soda in my hand. He apologised for not realising who I was when I telephoned, saying that he now remembered me very well. Considering the violence done to my appearance by Jennifer this didn't ring true. Carlos was plainly lying, but I assumed he was just being polite. After all, as far as I knew he was just a Venezuelan businessman who was at a bit of a loose-end in a foreign city and was spectacularly bad at cards. I had no idea that I was sitting in the operational headquarters of the Commando Boudia of the Popular Front for the Liberation of Palestine, or that my poker partner would soon be the world's most wanted international terrorist - Carlos the Jackal.

***

'I raise you $500,' hisses Carlos, his mouth an ugly snarl. He sheds a card and takes another. I check and call. He scrutinises the new hand and a smile creeps across his features. With a triumphant flourish, Carlos lays out his cards in a fan. A full house – a pair of Jacks and three sixes. Not bad. But I have a royal flush.

'Shit!' bellows Carlos. He pounds the low wooden table with his fist so that it shakes and creaks. Like everything else in the squalid studentish flat, it was shoddy and stained.

Carlos leans back. The beige velour sofa on which he sits is blotched with scars inflicted by coffee stains and cigarette scorchings. He lights a *Stuyvesant International*, an extravagantly elongated cigarette advertised at the time as the passport to the jet-set. A private joke on the part of the doyen of aircraft hi-jackers, I now suspect.

Carlos wears a milk-chocolate coloured corduroy suit and a poncy black voile shirt. The shirt is open at the neck with three buttons undone revealing a gold medallion, like a discotheque Lothario. But he must be even more disconcerted by my appearance. In retrospect, I think that Jennifer's efforts to disguise me may have counted much in my favour with Carlos and persuaded him that I was a suitable candidate for the task he had in mind. In fact, if I'd turned up decently dressed that evening I might never have walked out of there alive.

'We Latinos, we like to win at games,' says Carlos sullenly. 'Everyone knows that the English enjoy losing. But you, you keep winning. It's not right.'

'Sorry, old chap, lady luck seems to be sitting on my lap tonight.'

'The slut,' spits Carlos.

I shrug. 'There's always the next hand,' I say, lighting up a *Lucky strike*, the brand I've adopted since my arrival in France as a sort of talisman.

'How much I owe you?'

'$6,000, I'm afraid.'

'Maybe I kill you,' says Carlos, with a cruel sneer. 'I know a man who would kill you for $5,000. Perhaps even $4,000. Killing you is cheaper than paying you.'

'But then you wouldn't have anyone to play poker with.'

Carlos likes the reply. He laughs. He rocks back and forth on the sofa guffawing and slapping his thigh, upsetting a mug poised on an arm-rest that administers the evening's quota of coffee dregs.

'OK, I give you the money,' he says. He reaches into a jacket pocket and pulls out a fat wad of dollar bills bound by a rubber band. Plucking some notes, he slaps them down on the table. I gather-up my booty immediately, just in case he changes his mind. By now I've realised there is something sinister, even deranged, about Carlos.

'No more poker, tonight,' says Carlos waving a finger. 'Now we drink. Now we talk.'

He walks over to the sideboard, a hideous, modern, Formica-covered white coffin, supported by spindly black metal legs. On top is a tin tray hosting half-a-dozen tall tumblers festooned with little white flowers, the tacky sort they give away in petrol stations, a matching water-jug, an ice bucket masquerading as a plastic pineapple and a bottle of Courvoisier. He pours a couple of stiff ones on-the-rocks and hands one to me.

'Down the hatch,' I say, cordially raising my glass.

Carlos grunts as he slumps heavily on to the sofa, a glass in one hand the bottle of Courvoisier in the other. He takes a serious swig and torches another *Stuyvesant*. He stares at me intently, motionlessly, like a cat stalking a songbird. I gaze back. We are locked eyeball to eyeball in a contest of wills. I take in every detail of his face. The eyes, watery-white with flecks of green, like boiled cabbage. The tubby cheeks, as pasty as mashed potatoes. The lips, pale pink like boiled gammon. Add it all up and you have a plate of school dinner. I start laughing at the thought – I can't help myself. And then Carlos joins in, happy in the belief that he has out-stared me and won the game. That he is top dog.

He refreshes his glass from the bottle of Courvoisier.

'So, what are you *really* doing in Paris, Johnny?' he
enquires.

'Like I said before, I'm writing a novel,' I reply. I am puzzled. I thought we'd already settled that subject.

He scrutinises me sceptically.

'Don't give me that crap. We know all about you, Johnny.'

'What do you mean?'

'We know you're on the run. We know your real identity.
But we don't understand why you contacted us?'

'I need money,' I say. 'You are right. I am on the run. I
can't go near my friends or draw on my bank account. I
thought I might win some dosh playing poker. I had your
visiting card in my wallet, so I rang you.'

Carlos weighs up my answer.

'I believe you, Johnny,' he says at last. 'Tell me what are
you going to do now?'

'I'm going away. Far away.'

'Marie went through your clothes and your luggage. You
have no proper passport, just a shitty little Visitor's visa in a
phony name.'

'I'm going to buy a passport on the black market with the
money I won tonight. Then, maybe Australia.'

'You're lucky to have got this far, but even $6,000 isn't
going to get you safely to Australia. You're a wanted man,
Johnny. Life's expensive when you're a fugitive. The guy you
buy the passport from, for instance, he'll blackmail you. So
will all the others who realise that you're not who you pretend
to be. You need big bucks, Johnny. You need friends. I can
help you. You see, I need someone with your experience.'

'Play more often, that's my advice.'

'What?'

'Get a regular poker game going with some of your friends.
As they say, practice makes perfect.'

Carlos looks at me sternly, the harshness back in his face.

'No more stupid jokes, Johnny.' He takes a pistol from a shoulder holster and puts it on the table in front of him.

'Alright,' I croak, my throat drying-up as I stare in horror at the weapon. 'I'll tell you all I know.'

So Carlos isn't a good loser, after all. He'll let me keep my winnings only if I teach him every trick in the book.

'Now listen, Johnny. We need an insider. Someone who knows Westminster and the government's games. You will be very useful to us in London. Of course, we'll make it worth your while.'

True enough, as an hereditary peer the House of Lords, at least, is familiar turf, though why Carlos wants to play poker with members of parliament is voodoo to me. There are much better games elsewhere in town. But returning to Britain is out of the question.

'I can't go back,' I object. 'I'll be arrested immediately.'

'Wrong. My organisation will provide you with a false passport. A good one, not the amateur sort you buy in some bar on the black market. You have already altered your appearance, I observe. You will be safe enough.'

'Look,' I say rising from my chair, 'I'd love to help you improve your game, but it's getting very late. I really must be going.'

Carlos looks at me icily. He picks up the pistol and points it at my forehead.

'Do you think we're just going to let you walk out of here, Mr Stonehouse?'

I sit down sharply, my gaze fixed on the barrel of the gun. My mind is reeling. I realise that he must be muddling me with the other famous fugitive of the moment, John Stonehouse. I'm a bit narked at the thought of being mistaken for a member of the Other Place and a socialist? But, I'm in no position to protest, and, after all, Carlos *is* a foreigner.

'What do you have in mind?' I enquire meekly.

'You will help us assassinate Harold Wilson,' declares Carlos grinning heartily.

Suddenly all is clear. His dastardly plan is to send fugitive cabinet minister John Stonehouse back to Britain to assist a hit squad to kill the Prime Minister.

★★★

And so began my short career as an international terrorist.

2. *Death By Chocolate*

I'll wager a pony, or even a monkey, that I am the first and only peer of the realm to have woken up on his fortieth birthday in an Arab terrorist training camp in the Yemeni desert, but that's where I found myself on 18th December 1974.

Gently humming *Happy Birthday To You*, I tiptoed over to the window and watched the desert dawn. It was a magnificent spectacle, the spreading splash of yellow turning to the ultramarine sky to crimson and azure and the purple earth to ochre. I was so entranced that for a few moments forgot my troubles. I felt relaxed and revitalised – 'born again' as our old padre, the Reverend McVitie, was wont to say – and ready for whatever the future might hold.

The spell of the sunrise was broken by grunts and snuffling from the bed a few yards away as Anwer, my minder, shifted in his sleep. Our quarters was a white-walled, wood-floored hut, furnished only with a couple of cast iron beds and wooden lockers for our kit – just like a British barrack. In fact, it had been a British barrack until we'd pulled out of Aden in the '60s. Now it was home to a gang of gunmen.

Anwer had been assigned to me when I'd arrived a week earlier. He was tall and gangly-limbed, with the downy and pimply complexion of a train-spotter, though in fact he was in his twenties. He was fit as a ferret and I quickly dismissed thoughts of outrunning or overpowering him to make an escape. He spoke excellent English, having spent some years as an engineering student at London University. As a result, he was something of an Anglophile, waxing lyrical about pork pies and Scotch eggs and being a big fan of James Bond films. But his real passion was Elvis Presley and he was forever whistling *Wooden Heart*, a maddening habit. His academic studies, although not completed, had not been wasted: he had put them to practical purpose manufacturing bombs for my hosts.

The days at the camp were filled with a variety of forms of instruction. Weapons training with Soviet-bloc small arms – Makarov and Tokarev pistols, M24 sub machine guns, Kalashnikov AK47s, SVD Dragunov rifles and the rest – was fun. They had an extensive cache and I was able to have a go on many models I'd never seen before. I've always been a passable shot and acquitted myself well on the firing range, getting a gold star from the instructor. Then there were classes on cloak and dagger stuff straight out of a John le Carré novel, such as dead-letter drops and rules about making contact with one's controller. Anwer himself conducted the lessons on explosives, explaining how to make car bombs, letter bombs and below-the-belt anti-personnel devices, dastardly stuff they didn't teach one at Sandhurst.

He had orders never to let me out of his sight and he followed them to the letter. He even accompanied me to the thunder-box, skulking outside the cubicle. Damn disconcerting. In public he was a bit of a martinet, barking commands at me in a showy way. But in the privacy of the hut he was perfectly civil and sometimes even considerate enough to turn down the radio that blared out Arab music day and night. He delighted in playing with bits of wire, batteries and parts from dismantled alarm clocks and his enthusiasm was almost infectious. On the other hand he had a remarkable capacity for looking on the dark side and from time to time was a real moaning minnie. Yet he was not entirely without a sense of humour, but of fifth-form level and his laugh was an exasperating high-pitched titter. He was what Gussie and Boy would have called a twerp.

★★★

Comrade Mahoud, the camp commander, a powerfully-built man who dressed in a khaki shirt with epaulettes and sported a droopy moustache, was standing at the window of his office gazing through the slatted blinds towards the hills. The room was spacious, light and airy, a large overhead fan that might well have once graced the nose of a bi-plane generating a gentle breeze. Turning as we entered, Mahoud greeted us warmly. He invited us to sit down, indicating a couple of rattan-covered arm chairs with a sweep of the arm, though he himself remained standing, strolling up and down the room as we talked.

He was in a merry mood. 'Your leader has the shits,' he said chuckling and handed me an English newspaper. An article circled in red ink was headlined *Wilson Sick After Eating Oysters With President Giscard d'Estang at Elysée Palace.*

'Poor old Harold,' I said, feigning both friendship and concern.

'Your instructors report that you have learned well,' said Mahoud, addressing me. 'That is good, because your training is over. You both leave here in one hour. The time for action has come. From now on you will be known by the code-name "Commando Graceland". The name is Anwer's choice.'

He picked up the pair of passports lying on his desk and handed one each to Anwer and myself. Mine was Jamaican, a dignified document, dark blue with gold lettering. Turning the pages, I found a photo of myself taken at the camp a few days earlier. Below was my new name.

'Toots du Maurier,' I spluttered. 'What sort of a name is that?'

'A Jamaican name,' responded Mahoud in an injured tone

of voice, as if I was questioning his organisation's compe-
tence. 'It's a *genuine* Jamaican passport.'

'Who is Toots du Maurier?'

'Some Jamaican,' said Mahoud with a shrug. 'Don't worry,
he won't bother you. He's dead. Very dead. Shot in a dispute
between drug dealers and his body professionally disposed of
by the Mafia.'

'But why a Jamaican? I'm not black.'

'There are white Jamaicans too,' interjected Anwer. 'There
was one of them on my university course in London.'

'Jamaicans don't need visas to enter Britain,' Mahoud
explained, 'which makes it easy for you to come and go.'

'I can't go back to Britain. I'm a wanted man there.'

'John Stonehouse is a wanted man. Toots du Maurier is
just a Jamaican visitor,' said Mahoud slowly and emphatically, his hand coming to rest on the handle of the pistol that
protruded from a holster on his hip. He regarded me coldly.
There was no *bonhomie* in his eyes any more; there was
menace and ruthlessness. 'Of course, if you refuse . . .'

'No, no. You make the point most persuasively.'

'Good. You will fly to Rome this morning where you will
buy tickets for the next plane to London. You will stay at a
safe house – Anwer knows where – and await instructions.'

'To assassinate Wilson?'

'Exactly.'

'But why?'

'How can you ask such a question,' said Mahoud angrily.
'He is an enemy of the Palestinian people. A running dog of
the international Zionist capitalist conspiracy of world domi-
nation. A poodle of American imperialism. Wilson must die,'
he howled, hammering the desk with his fist. 'We will cut him
down like a dog.'

I stared at him, speechless with astonishment. Mahoud
was barking, so to speak.

'You have nothing to say?' enquired Mahoud, breaking the silence that had followed his outburst. He was staring at me intensely, his glare full of malevolence. 'Perhaps you too are a Zionist agent? A hyena in our midst? You know what we do with spies?' A cruel smile snaked across his lips. 'We take them down to . . .'

'Death to the mongrel Wilson,' I shouted with as much fanatical fervour as I could muster, being eager to divert his train of thought. 'Death to Great Danes, Red Setters, Spaniels, Dachshunds, Jack Russells, Pekinese . . .'

'Maybe after Wilson, we liquidate Crufts,' suggested Anwer.

'Great idea,' I replied, continuing playacting, 'but one thing at a time. I hope that you realise that Wilson is very closely guarded because of the IRA bombing campaign that's going on in London at the moment. How are you going to get past all those security Johnnies?'

'You will help us,' replied Mahoud coolly. 'You were a member of Wilson's government. You will tell us how to do it, Mr Stonehouse.'

The full brilliance of their plan was now clear; of course Stonehouse would know how to get to Wilson. I – or, rather, my alter ego – was indispensable to them. I had no choice but to co-operate, and it would be woe betide me if they ever found out that I wasn't who they thought I was.

'I'll do my best,' I said as perkily as I could, hoping to hide my fears.

'We're relying on you,' said Mahoud leaning forward so that I got a hot blast of his *merguez*-tainted breath. 'Remember, either Wilson dies or you do. *Bon voyage*, Mr Stonehouse.'

★★★

I'd sometimes wondered while diverting myself with those

spy stories what a 'safe house' was actually like. Now I knew. For a start, it wasn't a *house*, but a low-rent basement flat in Earls Court. And *safe*, meant forlorn and mouse-infested. Access was by a narrow and precipitous set of steps that led down from the pavement to a door underneath the porch of the large white stucco Victorian house that loomed above. Inside, immediately to the right of the front door, there was a kitchen where the amenities were a couple of grubby gas rings, chipped yellow Formica surfaces and a big battleship-grey metal sink whose taps sported perished and discoloured pink rubber nozzles. Turning left, there was a long shadowy corridor lit by a single 40 watt bulb in a dangling globe lamp-shade with an orange floral pattern that glowed like a Hal-loween pumpkin. Anwer locked the front door behind us and stepped over to my side. 'Toilet. Your room. My room. Lounge,' he said pointing into the gloom at the doors off the passageway, far end first.

My bedroom was furnished and decorated in seaside boarding house style. The walls were covered in sepia hessian and the carpet had a fussy red and black motif. The bed was designed to preclude hanky-panky, not to mention sleep. Not only was it so short that my feet protruded off the end, but the mattress undulated irregularly and the pillows were filled with foam rubber rocks. The bedspread was magenta tow-elling, to match the curtains. By the headboard was a spindly bamboo side-table on which was a lamp made out of a Chi-anti bottle, its singed shade depicting a range of Italian wine labels. A pretty dismal dump, but a whole lot better than a Dartmoor prison cell.

The sitting room was similarly furnished. The sagging sofa was covered in a dingy orange and chocolate floral print, as were the pair of fagged-out armchairs. The wallpaper featured great swirling dishwater-coloured brush marks, the curtains a brown and green twig and leaf motif in the style of

William Morris and the carpet a series of yellow, red and rust splodges like a close-up of a Monet canvas. Commando Graceland's HQ had an interior decor from Hell.

Anwer was sprawled on the sofa watching the TV news. A reporter was describing the clearing-up operations in London after the large-scale damage done by three IRA car bombs the previous evening.

'This town is full of crazies,' Anwer moaned twerpishly. 'They've sent us to a war-zone. I could get killed.'

The subject changed to a report on the fighting between Frelimo guerrillas and government forces in the Portuguese colony of Mozambique. Anwer glanced at his watch. He rose and put on his overcoat hurriedly.

'Where are you going?' I asked.

'It's time to call Carlos.'

'Why don't you use that 'phone?' I pointed at the instrument on the sideboard.

'Don't you remember your training? You never call your controller from your own 'phone. It might be bugged. Anyway, it doesn't work. Comrade Carlos forgot to pay the bill and it was cut off.'

I watched him ascend the outside steps and disappear along the pavement. As soon as he was gone I tried the front door. Locked, of course. I checked every window. All were robustly barred. I even lifted the telephone receiver, but the line was dead just as he'd said. There was no escape. So that's what a *safe house* was – a prison.

***

'Carlos is coming round tomorrow afternoon,' Anwer announced upon his return a couple of hours later. 'He's impatient to hear your plans to kill Wilson. I hope you've got some good ideas. He's not very nice when he's angry.'

'I've been thinking about it while you were out. Tomorrow

morning I'll phone Downing Street posing as a journalist writing an article about how top people are spending Christmas and get details of his movements. When I know what he's up to I'll be able to suggest a course of action.'

'That should please Carlos,' said Anwer, as he emptied the contents of a large plastic carrier bag on to the sitting room table. There was a loaf of sliced white bread, a pint of milk, frozen peas, tinned peaches, Scotch eggs and pork pies, a brace of bottles of Famous Grouse whisky, several packets of Dunhill, the magazine *What's On In London* and some long-playing records. There were two Elvis Presley's, *Sheer Heart Attack* by some shower called Queen, and *Rollin'* by a bunch of street arabs styled the Bay City Rollers. I remarked sarcastically that I wasn't familiar with these so-called artists. I soon would be, Anwer replied. What I meant, was that I never listened to pop music; I detested it, except for a few tuneful ballads. What he meant was that he was going to play the records full blast; which was just what he did.

★★★

'So, we meet again,' said Carlos, extending his hand to me as he stepped into the sitting room. He lowered a heavy-looking grey canvas holdall from his shoulder on to the table where it crumpled with a dull sigh.

'I've got you a Mauser automatic and a Styr-Mannlicher SSG sniper rifle with telescopic sight,' he informed Anwer. 'There's also two M26 grenades and some slabs of plastic explosive.'

Anwer dipped into the bag and pulled out the hand gun. He checked the magazine and the safety clasp, and put it in the shoulder holster he was wearing under his jacket. Then he carried the bag over to the metal safe that stood in a corner of the room and locked it inside.

'You want to keep a close eye on this guy,' said Carlos

pointing at me from the armchair in which he was now loung-ing. 'He's dangerous. He took $6,000 off me at poker one night. He's got the luck of the Devil.'

'I found out already,' said Anwer sourly. The cards had not gone his way the night before.

'You too,' said Carlos with a howl of laughter. 'Well Mr Stonehouse, I hope you're as good at assassinations as at cards. How do we get Wilson?'

'Wilson's movements over the Christmas period are as fol-lows: he's spending Christmas Day at Chequers, his official residence in Kent; on Boxing Day evening he drives to Lon-don and takes an overnight train from Paddington station to Penzance, Cornwall; in the morning he's picked up and taken to a nearby Royal Navy base and flown by helicopter to the Scilly Isles where he has a holiday home. He's spending a week there. Then he returns to Downing Street.'

Carlos nodded. 'So where does the hit take place?', he asked slowly and thoughtfully.

'Chequers is too well-guarded. Penzance and the Scilly Isles are cut off and present difficulties for making an escape. The best moment is when he arrives at Paddington Station. There might just be an opportunity for a sniper to have a shot, like in *Day of the Jackal*. Mind you, Paddington will be crawl-ing with police and SAS. It will be very risky for you.'

'Not for me. For you.'

'Me?'

'You are a crack shot. I've seen the training camp report on your marksmanship.'

'I never agreed to kill anyone.'

'We're not playing cricket, Mr Stonehouse. You shoot Wilson, or I shoot you.'

Now, this was a development I had anticipated. What's more, I had worked out a stratagem for getting myself off the hook.

'Suppose, there was another way? A more subtle and more reliable method. Wouldn't that be better?'

'A nuclear bomb, maybe,' suggested Carlos sniggering.

'Poison.'

'Poison!' exclaimed Anwer aghast. 'We're international terrorists. We blow things up and shoot people. We're not murderers.'

'Anwer's right, poison isn't our style,' said Carlos disdainfully. 'We have our standing to consider. We'd be a laughing stock in the eyes of the Red Army Faction or the Baader-Meinhof gang. Anyway, how do you propose to administer the poison? Dress up as a waitress and serve him *soupe a la strychnine*?' He chuckled at his suggestion and Anwer joined in.

'Remember Wilson's food poisoning at the Elysée? What could be more natural than for President Giscard to give him a Christmas present to make amends. Such an offering would sail through security without problems. And what could be more appropriate than a *bûche de Noël au chocolat*?'

'What's that?'

'A traditional French Christmas cake. The English call it a Yule Log. It's a long cylindrical-shaped *gâteau* covered in chocolate. Wilson loves sweets. He won't be able to resist having a nibble when its delivered to him at Chequers on Christmas morning.'

'He overdoses on chocolate?'

'He dies of poisoning. The Yule Log is laced with poison.'

'Where do you get these things?'

'Harrods, of course. And they'll deliver it too, along with a note we'll provide, explaining that it comes from the French president as a present for the prime minister.'

'They'll put in the poison too?'

'You'll have to do that. You bring it back here, add the poison and then return it saying that there has been a mix-up and that it should have been delivered to Chequers. They'll accept that. At Harrods the customer is always right.'

'Why not a bomb?' interjected Anwer, in an awe-struck tone of voice. 'We fill the cake full of explosive and blow him to Hell.'

'That's much better,' said Carlos brightly. 'We set the time fuse for lunch time. And then BANG – death by chocolate! We'll go down in the history books for this,' he said to Anwer who was wearing a wide grin.

'Death by chocolate,' intoned Anwer. 'It's beautiful. Just beautiful.'

★★★

That evening Anwer was in high spirits. I had learnt that a sure-fire sign that the twerp was in a good mood was when he started banging-on about stuff he'd read in his Elvis fan club magazines. I had also leant that he got into a serious bate if I didn't show what he considered to be proper attention. Tonight's lecture was about Elvis's extensive collection of police department badges. Most improbably, the singer had a fixation about the police and had persuaded forces the length and breadth of the US to make him an honorary patrolman or sergeant. He'd even been made an honorary special agent of the Federal Bureau of Narcotics personally by President Nixon.

Anwer interrupted his speech to fetch a bottle of Famous Grouse from the kitchen and fix us some drinks. While he played barman, I rifled through the pages of *What's On In London* desperate to find a way of sparing myself the next instalment and further earfuls of Queen and the Bay City Rollers.

'I say, *The Man With The Golden Gun* has opened in the West End,' I gushed. In fact, my enthusiasm was genuine. I've always enjoyed James Bond films. Rattling good yarns, and also because I was almost screen-tested for the part of Bond by Cubby Broccoli the producer. An innate reserve made me decline the invitation, but I was ever curious to see what I might have got mixed up in. Of course, I couldn't explain my interest to Anwer without raising suspicions about my true identity.

'Tonight?' he asked.

'Yes, but we'll have to hurry.'

Anwer's face lit up. 'Right. Drink up,' he commanded, guzzling his glass as he struggled into his coat.

Commando Graceland strode briskly along side streets until we came to the Old Brompton Road. We stood on a corner next to a large Victorian pub called the Coleherne Arms waiting for a cab. We were not alone. Despite the cold, there was a bevy of men loitering around outside staring into space. They all seemed to be dressed in black leather jackets twinned with denim blue-jeans or leather trousers with flaps like cinema cowboys. They all had drooping moustaches. Silver studs were a popular embellishment of their jackets and their belts, from which hung bunches of keys and in some cases pairs of handcuffs. Every now and then someone went into or came out the pub which seemed to serve as a sort of hive. Then a cab arrived and carried us off to the West End.

Approaching from Marble Arch, Oxford Street shimmered ahead in the night like a rhinestone bracelet laid on a black velvet cloth. It had stopped raining only minutes earlier and the road was glassy and colourful from the reflections of the Christmas illuminations strung overhead. The gleam of headlights and fire-fly tail-lights danced around us. The acres of shop windows on both sides of the road were full of twinkling fairy lights, glittering tinsel and sparkling foil. Everywhere there were fir trees, snowflakes, holly and mistletoe, reindeer and the Godfather of the whole industry, Santa himself.

My musings were interrupted by an almighty explosion

behind us. The cab bucked violently and came to an abrupt halt. Anwer and I flew into the air, hit the roof and ricocheted into a tangled mess on the floor.

'What you up to in the back there?, carped the cabby looking into his rear-view mirror, presumably wondering where his fares were hiding.

'What happened?' moaned Anwer as we struggled up on to the seat.

'Must be them IRA bastards,' said the cabby matter-of-factly. 'Bloody lousy for trade all these damn bombs.'

Suddenly the still silence that had immediately followed the blast was replaced by a chorus of sirens, shop alarms and screaming, the night music of the urban jungle. The ground all around was strewn with glass shimmering like hail from Hell. Overhead the shattered decorations dangled like gibbets.

'Get me out of here,' screamed Anwer. 'I want to go home.'

***

We arrived back at the flat without further incident. As soon as we got through the front door Anwer dived into the kitchen and re-emerged swigging from a bottle of Famous Grouse. Shaking and ashen he slumped down on the sofa in the sitting room. I was bemused by his behaviour. Being under fire isn't everyone's cup of tea, but shell-shock was a trifle rich coming from the lips of a self-styled international terrorist.

'Anwer, why did you become a terrorist?' I enquired gently, reflecting that a supermarket check-out clerk or a short-order chef were more fitting occupations for the twerp.

'To save my family's honour,' he replied. And then the whole story cascaded-out like a confession. He was the son of a respectable family in one of the most religiously orthodox of the Gulf states. Naturally, he had never tasted pork and upon his arrival in London he had developed what he described as an addiction to this forbidden fruit. Returning home one university vacation, his luggage had been searched at customs and the pork pies he had packed for furtive feasts were discovered. They were seized for offending against the Koranic proscription of the consumption of pig meat and he was indicted for attempting to smuggle profane articles. The impending court case threatened his family with disgrace and so he took the Beau Geste option – he bolted and joined-up with the vernacular equivalent of the French Foreign Legion.

★★★

There was no stirring from Anwer the next morning. By lunch time I was so ravenous I was starting to have hallucinogenic fantasies about lamb cutlets. Being able to stand it no longer, I woke him up, volunteering to go out foraging for breakfast if he'd give me the key. He refused, saying that Carlos would kill him if he came round and found that I'd been let loose on my own. Then he'd kill me. To which I replied that since I was about to expire from hunger it didn't make much difference. Eventually he pulled himself together, returning from the outside world with something only slightly less foul than his own 'home cooking' which we hungrily devoured.

We waited in all day for Carlos to appear as arranged, but he never showed up. Anwer spent the time skulking in the sitting room moaning about his hangover, and playing pop records at full blast on the stereo. Finding the din unbearable, I retired to my bedroom and sat on the bed reading *Bring On The Empty Horses*, the second volume of David Niven's autobiography that I'd picked up at Rome airport. Nostalgic memories of the delightful sojourn at Cap Ferrat came flooding back to me, and I found myself bewailing the cruel twists of fate that had led me from a cosy billet on the *Cote d'Azur* to this grotty, clangorous, terrorist hideout in Earls Court.

A gunshot ran out in the sitting room. I was horror-struck, imagining that Anwer had decided to top himself. I rushed next door. He was sitting on the sofa gazing at the TV, whose shattered screen and blitzed ray-tube were strewn over the carpet.

'What have you done?'

'I blew him away.'

'Who?'

'Some bastard was justifying the bomb that almost killed us last night. He wasn't going to get away with that.'

'But he's on TV.'

'So? Elvis shoots out TVs when he hates the programme. So can I.'

It was no use arguing with that. What's more, he was holding a smoking gun.

'The difference is that the neighbours might take exception to the noise and call the police. And Carlos would be hopping mad,' I said, trying to terrify him back to reason. 'Look, why don't we go see that James Bond film. It would do us both good to get out of here for a bit.'

'Carlos ordered us to stay here.'

'Well it's eight o'clock already. He's had plenty of time to come round.'

'We might get killed out there.'

'Don't you know the saying, "lightning never strikes twice in the same place". So long as we stick to the same route as last night we'll be alright.'

He looked at me alertly, like I'd come up with the solution to a problem he'd been wrestling with.

'You're right. I feel like a rat in a cage in this place. Let's go.'

'I think you should leave the gun behind,' I said, having premonitions of him shooting up the screen if he didn't like Roger Moore's performance.

'No way. My instructions are to carry it all the time. You see, I have to shoot you if you try to do a runner.'

★★★

We're descending the steps leading to the flat after the flicks and a slap-up scoff in a Soho trattoria – *cotoletta di agnello* for yours truly – chateaued after a couple of bottles apiece. We're laughing and joking and feeling pretty much at one with the world for the first time in a fortnight. We reach the front door. Anwer fumbles with the key. He drops it in the flowerbed.

'Bugger Bognor', a phrase of George V's I'd taught him on the way home, he shouts as he fumbles about in the soil for it. We're killing ourselves laughing.

Something moves in the shadows. There's a man and he's holding a pistol. It's pointing at my head. I freeze. He steps forward into the pool of light cast by a street lamp. It's Carlos. He's scowling.

'You've kept me waiting, Commando Graceland,' he says icily. 'Where have you been?'

'To see a film,' Anwer answers sheepishly.

'I told you to wait in.'

'We waited all day. We can't stay cooped-up the whole time. It's driving me crazy.'

'You know the rules. Pleasure haunts are out of bounds to active service units, unless visited in the course of duty. You must be punished,' he says sinisterly. 'In future there will be no more going out to have fun – unless you take me too.'

Silence. We're both trying to make sense of what he means. The quiet is broken by a great guffaw from Carlos who reckons he's just pulled off an A1 practical joke. He isn't angry at all. He's just having fun giving us the willies. Then we all see the funny side. Ha! Ha! Ha!

Half an hour later we're in the sitting room polishing off a bottle of low flyer. The Three Musketeers are laughing and backslapping each other and making plans to go to a local disco tomorrow night – in the course of duty, of course. By the way, says Carlos, the Central Committee has approved our plan. We're going to turn Wilson into chocolate mousse. Ha! Ha! Ha!

***

As usual, I was woken by Anwer's blaring pop music, Elvis that morning. In fact, it was already late and he was impatient to get going, shouting for me to hurry up. As I showered I contemplated the wisdom of visiting a haunt such as Harrods where I might well bump into my chums, but the sight of myself in the shaving mirror dispelled any doubts. Not even Squiffy Marchmain would recognise his old mucker.

On the tube Anwer let slip that a visit to Harrods was a long-cherished ambition, second only to the Haj. And Knightsbridge was a lot nearer than Mecca.

He took to Harrods like a duck to water, wandering round goggle-eyed and open-mouthed like Ali Baba in the cave of the forty thieves. We explored the emporium from top to bottom, eventually arriving in the Food Halls. Anwer purred as he padded past cornucopias of fruit, an altar of seafood as sumptuous as a Baroque churchpiece, a baker's dozen squared of different sorts of loaves, and a swan carved out of ice rising out of a swathe of strawberries. Finally we came to the patisserie counter, Billy Bunter's ultimate fantasy.

'Is that what you mean?' asked Anwer, pointing at a chocolate cylinder about the size of a rolling pin surmounted by a Father Christmas with sleigh and reindeer sledding through icing sugar and sprigs of plastic holly.

'That's right,' It replied.

'Have you a bigger one?' he asked the sales assistant.

'We have,' she said indicating a real monster behind the counter about a yard long and with the diameter of a watering can, a veritable Moby Dick amongst Yule Logs. 'It was a special order for a customer who cancelled.'

'We'll take it,' said Anwer his eyes lighting up. 'It's just what we need for our big blow out.'

★★★

The entrance to the night-club was just like a normal front door and I would have passed-by oblivious. But Carlos was in the know and he strode up and pushed the buzzer. A panel in the door slid open and a pair of eyes spied us up and down. On Carlos's orders Anwer and I had gone shopping that afternoon and were now clad in black leather jackets and jeans. So we would be inconspicuous, he had explained. He himself was nattily attired in a Gestapo-style black leather greatcoat and a white roll-neck pullover.

The door opened and we stepped inside. The manager, properly-dressed in black tie, greeted Carlos like a regular and welcomed us as his guests.

Beyond the entrance lobby was a large, dark room deco-rated in reds and blacks with a rotating mirror-ball that shot shards of light snow-storming across the ceiling and walls. The music was loud. Very loud. Not a place I was likely to run into Squiffy Marchmain or Gussie and Boy, I reflected with relief.

We walked over to the bar and ordered some drinks. Carlos immediately set about chatting-up two girls with Latin American looks who were perched on bar stools. The man had a veritable passion for partying.

Anwer and I surveyed the scene, sipping the Bacardi and cokes that Carlos had commanded all round without asking for preferences. Over on the far side of the room the dance floor was a heaving throng. Nearer-by there were tables and chairs and some sofas on which people were sitting out, try-ing to talk above the din. Leather was very much the order of the day for both boys and girls and some of the clientele sported quaint accessories such as studded dog-collars, whips and handcuffs.

Anwer was watching the proceedings with an expression bewilderment and horror. He ordered another drink. A double. Plainly, the place was not his mug of Horlicks.

★★★

A bizarre figure clad in a black leather jump-suit plus Lone Ranger style face mask strides across the room towards me.

'You dance with me. You are my slave,' she says breathily, like a French actress. She grabs the lapel of my jacket and tugs me across the room.

We dance close, so close that our jackets squeak as leather rubs against leather. Her breasts caress my chest. She's running a leather riding crop up and down my back, with an occasional thwack. She whispers in my ear that she is going to spank my bare buttocks for being a naughty boy. There is something hauntingly familiar about the way she says the word *spank*.

'Jennifer? What on earth are you doing in a place like this? And dressed like that!' I jabber.

'I could ask you the same questions, but it doesn't matter. The important thing is we're together again, Lucky.'

'Don't call me that. My name is Toots.'

'Toots? What sort of a name is that?'

'Jamaican. I don't have time to explain. You've got to help me. I've been kidnapped. I'm here under duress.'

'You lucky boy. That's the sort of thing the rest of us here just dream about.'

'You don't understand. They're killers.'

'Who?'

'You see the man propping up the bar? And that one over there dancing with the two teenagers? They're my guards.'

'Well, let's make a run for it!'

'They'd kill us. These people are seriously wicked. The only chance is when they're not watching. Now, don't let on that you know me.'

'Whatever you say,' answers Jennifer as Carlos sidles up with his chicks and leads us back to the bar. He buys another round of drinks and holds court, while his hands rove across the bums of Lolita and Consuela. He's much amused by my pick-up and sniggers each time he looks at Jennifer in her bondage outfit. Anwer looks very unamused, like he's chewing lemons. Eventually, Carlos decrees that we're all going back to the flat. Jennifer too.

Carlos produces a bottle of Dom Perignon. He puts on a Rolling Stones record. We drink and dance, all except Anwer who skips the dancing. Eventually Carlos disappears with the *chiquitas* into Anwer's bedroom. Jennifer drags me off to my room. She strips and hands me her riding crop.

'Spank me,' she demands.

'Look it's late and I'm very tired . . .'

'Spank me or I'll scream.'

Wearily, with a deep sense of *deja vu*, I raise my hand, thinking what a funny old world it is.

★★★

Carlos and the girls had already left by the time Jennifer and I got up. Anwer was stretched out on the sofa fully dressed with a couple of coats for covers and his head on a cushion. For an instant I thought that it might be possible to remove the key from his sleeping body or even grab his gun, but no sooner had I taken a couple of steps than he was awake and watching me, pistol in hand.

'How are you feeling?' I asked breezily, setting a mug of *Nescafe* on the carpet next to the sofa.

'I've felt better,' he replied. I could believe it. He looked terrible.

'My friend has to leave now. I'd be grateful if you would let her out.'

He grunted. He slurped a mouthful of coffee and started to stir, slipping the gun out of sight as Jennifer came into the room.

'She suggests that we should meet her and a friend for a drink tonight.'

'She's very pretty and about your age,' added Jennifer. 'Her name is Natasha.'

There was a flicker of interest in Anwer's bleary bloodshot eyes.

'Fine,' he said.

Now, at last, I had an opportunity to give him the slip.

'Nine o'clock. And don't be late,' she commanded as we stood at the threshold. 'Byeeeeeeeee,' she intoned, scaling the steps and disappearing from view.

***

The rendezvous with Jennifer and Natasha was in a wine bar called Borsch & Tears. Alighting from the tube at Sloane Square, we strolled towards Beauchamp Place through the quiet back streets of Knightsbridge.

We were walking along Walton Street when a car drew up in front. A man jumped out and threw something about the size of a cricket ball through an upstairs window of one of the houses. He dived back inside the car which sped off at speed, tyres screeching, leaving a lingering odour of singed rubber. There was a flash and an explosion and glass showered down on us.

'Not again,' wailed Anwer. 'Run. We've got to get out of here. I'm carrying a gun.'

We scampered down a dark mews and kept on running until we reached the Kings Road.

'What about the girls?' I asked as we sheltered panting in

the shadowy back entrance of the Peter Jones department
store.

'To hell with them, we're going home,' said Anwer
adamantly. 'I'm never going out again in this madhouse
town.'

***

The sitting room table in the Earls Court basement flat was
covered in chocolate cake, the neatly hollowed-out innards of
the Yule Log. Anwer was in his element meticulously packing
the carcass of the cake with explosive and bits of wire.

I watched him for a while, but eventually got bored with
the spectacle and the blaring Queen record. Retiring to my
bedroom, I turned on the radio for some proper music.

My attention was riveted by the news bulletin announcement that a man had been arrested in Australia who was suspected of being the missing MP John Stonehouse. The game
was up. My cover was blown, and Carlos would blow me
away. My only hope was Jennifer. I had to get in touch with
her and tell her to send a posse of armed police to the flat to
arrest Lord Lucan.

I returned to the sitting room.

'I've been thinking about our conduct last night,' I said to
Anwer who was poking another wire into the cake. 'I feel very
guilty about standing up the girls. We owe them an apology.
I want to go out and ring Jennifer to say sorry.'

'No, no. No more dates. No more girls. We stay here. We
have work to do.'

'I can't accept that. This is a matter of honour. I cannot
live with this shame. You give me no option, but suicide.'

Anwer paused and looked up at me. His pained expression
told me that the concept of *honour* had hit home.

'OK, we go out and make one call. Then we come back
and we stay here. I'd fed up with being blown up.'

★★★

It was already dark outside and drizzling gently, prompting disparaging remarks about the dismal English weather from my companion. I picked up the hand-set in the phone box from which we usually made calls. No dialling tone. I then saw why – the wire was dangling down towards the ground unattached to the machine. It had been neatly sheared through.

'There's another one round the corner,' said Anwer. We moved on, but that one too had been vandalised in an identical way. We tried two more pavement call boxes, but it was the same story.

'In my country, we cut off the hands of people who do this,' said Anwer with more than a hint of exasperation in his voice.

'Let's try the pub. They might have a 'phone, I suggested, pointing at the Coleherne Arms up the road. I was becoming worried that he would decide to abandon the expedition and order us back to base. But he nodded agreement.

Inside, the pub was dingy and smoky. There was a great expanse of floor space with scarcely any tables or chairs. Men stood around, a few chatting despite the blaring pop music but most just loitered staring into space like their chums on the pavement. We strode over to the ornate Victorian bar and I asked the barman if there was a 'phone. He didn't even have time to begin replying before the most extraordinary thing happened.

Two sinister figures in sunglasses and black leather jackets loomed up to us, grabbing Anwer's arms and handcuffing his wrists to the bronze buffer-rail that ran along the front of the bar. He struggled and yelled like a stuck pig until his protests were muted by one of them removing the red and white bandanna round his neck and deftly turning it into a gag, knotting it at the back of Anwer's head.

'Happens all the time,' said the barman nonchalantly, with a shrug of the shoulders. 'Boys will be boys. By the way, the 'phone is down the other end of the bar.'

'Thanks, Roger and Nobby,' said a woman's voice, 'he's all yours.' It was Jennifer. 'Come on we've got to get going,' she said addressing me. 'My car is outside.'

I turned and waved good-bye to Anwer, but I don't think he noticed since at that moment he was performing a violent jig, trying to prevent the boys from applying a pair of leg irons.

We clambered into a red Mini conveniently parked round the corner in a quiet mews.

'What an extraordinary coincidence,' I exclaimed as we dived into the maelstrom of London traffic, 'that you and your friends happened to be having a drink in that strange pub.'

'Coincidence, my arse,' responded Jennifer. 'I knew you'd eventually come in to use the 'phone. We just had to be patient.'

'You mean it was you who vandalised all those 'phone boxes?'

'Of course. We did in dozens. You would have had to have walked for miles before you came to one that worked. It was only a matter of time before you decided to try the pub and we could rescue you.'

'I say, old sausage, you've saved my life,' I said humbly. 'I don't know how I can repay you.'

'I do,' said Jennifer as she put her foot down and we sped northwards towards the cottage she had borrowed from a friend for our Yuletide love nest . . .

3. Castro's Classroom

My favourite hotel? The Ritz, London? The George V, Paris? The Plaza, New York? The Negresco, Nice? None of them. The Polana, Maputo, or Lourenço Marques as it was called when I first stayed there. Built in the early years of the century by Portuguese colonials, it's a stately structure in a formal classical style. The facade is wedding-cake white stucco, ornamented with crisp pilasters, arches and balustrades. The central part is flanked by two wings that fan out at an angle, like an altar triptych, reminding one of the splendid Hotel du Cap on the Cap Ferrat headland. But the Polana has an even more magnificent location, perched atop a cliff looking out over the azure sea of the Bay of Maputo. It's surrounded by lawns dotted with tall palms and gardens full of butterflies and brightly plumed songbirds. A little bit of heaven on earth; but in April 1975, there was trouble in paradise.

Mozambique was in the throes of the transfer of power from the colonial administration to the victorious Frelimo guerrillas at the end of a long and bloody war. Although Lourenço Marques itself was mostly unscathed by the fighting, the country was bust and even the necessities of life were in short supply. Mind you, I found that by paying in US dollars one was inconvenienced remarkably little. Of course, this didn't apply to electricity or running water, but the hotel staff sustained supplies of most things with commendable enterprise.

The tension in Lourenço Marques during this no-mans-

time was almost tangible, looks and words being rife with suspicion and double-meaning. Soon after my arrival a plot was
discovered amongst officers of the Portuguese Army to stop
the handover to Frelimo. Fearful of a backlash, many of the
colonials upped sticks for Portugal or South Africa and the
hotel became almost deserted. But soon it was full again, not
of the prosperous Portuguese planters and suave Lisbon
bankers of yore, but of a scallywag crew of grey-suited, grim-
faced Soviet bloc diplomats, flash-Harry black marketeers
with loud ties and loud mouths, sleazy bloodsuckers profiting
from the misfortunes and misery of others, and a rat-pack of
journalists who never ventured further than the pool and
invented their copy in the bar.

I suppose that readers will want to know how I found
myself there. I spent Christmas and New Year lying low with
Jennifer in a cottage in Borehamwood, Hertfordshire. But
being cooped-up, unable to go outside for fear of being recognised now that I'd ditched my absurd disguise, began to fray
my nerves. It was time to make a move, to somewhere I could
live more freely. What's more, after a few weeks of Jennifer's
hospitality I was severely in need of a holiday. Money and
passport were no longer a problem, both having been supplied by Carlos and his cronies. However, it was now doubly
dangerous for me to leave the country by conventional routes,
having both the British police and a gang of international terrorists after my skin.

Every means of flight seemed fraught with hazard, but then
I remembered that a friend, Graham Hill, the well-known
Formula One racing driver, kept a private plane that he used
for his frequent trips to the continent, piloting the aircraft
himself. An additional advantage of this scheme was that
being a two-seater it would be impossible for Jennifer to come
too, as she had in mind. Life on the run would be far too dangerous for a woman, I told myself. Besides, the punishing

pace of our boudoir romps was doing worrying mischief to my lumbar vertebrae, not to mention the fleshy mischief she got up to with the fly-swat and other domestic implements.

Graham Hill was informed that his passenger, Monsieur du Maurier, was a French motor-mechanic who was urgently need at Le Mans. Imagine then his amazement when I tore off my Biggles-style flying helmet, a present from Jennifer, and revealed my true identity. So surprised and so delighted was he to see me that he performed a celebratory loop-the-loop, receiving a reprimand from air traffic control for his exuberance. After refuelling in France we touched down in northern Portugal where I bid him farewell.

I proceeded to Lisbon by train. Portuguese friends sheltered me with their generous hospitality and arranged for my passage to Lourenço Marques. Just as predicted, the last thing on anyone's mind as the city awaited the transfer of power to the Frelimo rebels was a fugitive English aristocrat. It was a perfect place to lie doggo.

★★★

Raoul Matanzas cut a distinctive figure amongst the regulars in the bar of the Polana Hotel. His appearance was distinctly *ancien régime* and I warmed to him immediately. He was slim and tall, almost as tall as me, with a handsome tanned face, greying hair and effortless charm. Neatly dressed in a belted stone-grey tropical suit and white shirt, he chain-smoked *Kools* through an ivory cigarette holder. He spoke good English, though with a strong Latin-American accent, and told me that he had studied History of Art at the Fogg Institute at Harvard before the Revolution. The Cuban Revolution, that was. Now he was Cuban cultural envoy to Mozambique and his mission was to forge 'cultural solidarity' with the people, whatever that meant. He asked if I knew his close friend Anthony Blunt, but the name meant nothing to me at the time.

Raoul was more than a little inquisitive about the reasons for my presence in Lourenço Marques. I deflected his questions with vague phrases about being an international businessman in 'import-export', lines I'd learnt from Carlos. One evening our conversation turns to guns, the Art historian aesthete surprising me with his knowledge of Soviet small arms. A hobby, so he claimed. We debated the merits of the Radom Wz35 pistol versus the Tokarev TT33, the SVD Dragunov and the M54 as sniper rifles, and even got onto such esoterics as the UBM52 heavy mortar and the RPG7 anti-tank free flight missile launcher. I gave a good account of myself thanks to my first hand experiences at the training camp in the Yemen, and was even able to correct him on a few points.

At our next encounter, Raoul hit another coconut when he raised the subject of gambling. He quizzed me closely about all the casino games and was very complimentary about the extent of my knowledge. Our talk turned to poker and it soon became clear that Raoul was no novice like Carlos. A friendship emerged from our conversations and shared mutual interests. It also occurred to me that Raoul could provide just the sort of support I needed to establish the poker game that was the key to the replenishment of my coffers.

★★★

It soon became a habit to lunch at Peveri, the best place in town for piri-piri prawns, which I had taken to as a substitute for lamb cutlets, sadly not available. My regular luncheon companion was Maria, a distant cousin of my Portuguese friends. Maria was an absolute stunner, with a trim figure, full breasts, long dark hair, wide opalescent eyes and ripe pouting lips. She was a teacher of English, but had plenty of time on her hands because the school where she worked had been closed by the authorities on account of the civil disorder. Her help was invaluable to me during my sojourn in Lourenço Marques and in return I offered to give her English lessons in the afternoons. I had just got into my stride in explaining the rules of cricket, when she pounced. She ripped off my clothes in a frenzy of Latin passion and we made torrid love in the position of the Portuguese-Man-of-War, a new one for me. Dash it, that girl could teach even Jennifer a thing or two. It is still on my conscience that in the heat of the moment I entirely overlooked mentioning the crucial leg-before-wicket regulation.

One day our lunch at Peveri was interrupted by a stranger, who strode up to the table and demanded to know if I was English. Naturally I was suspicious, fearing a police trap particularly since he was accompanied by a mean-mugged bulldog, which, for reasons I cannot identify, brought to mind Squiffy Marchmain. Thinking quickly I told him that I was Italian, putting on a phoney accent inspired by Marlon Brando's performance in *The Godfather*. With my natural dark colouring, my suntan and my shades I certainly looked plausibly Italian. I invited him to join us, wanting to discover why he was interested in me.

He turned out to be a homesick general practitioner from Cardiff, called Brian. He explained that it was rare to hear English spoken in Lourenço Marques and he had fancied a chat in his native language, which seemed plausible enough at the time. He soon had us spell-bound with the tale of his recent journey to Lourenço Marques from Swaziland through guerrilla infested deserts and swamps, his life being saved on more than one occasion by his trusty companion, Nipper. Stealthily I turned the conversation to cards. He told that he enjoyed a game of poker, though he played rather badly. I invited him for a drink at the Polana Hotel bar. I had found my meal-ticket.

Brian turned up after dinner as arranged. I'd already got a

game going in a corner of the bar with Raoul and a few of the
other renegades and rascals when he joined us. I was doing
pretty well and was already a couple of hundred dollars better
off. But Brian made all the difference and by the time he
threw in the towel my winnings were well on the way to a
thousand. The others drifted away and soon there was only
Brian and me left. He was looking distinctly down in the
mouth and suggested an expedition into town to a lively bar
he knew by the docks. Feeling a little guilty about the fleec-
ing I'd inflicted, I agreed to accompany him.

It was a pleasantly balmy evening, the air fragrant with the
scent of frangipani and jasmine. But the streets were deserted
save for our taxi, the inhabitants being too terrified to set foot
outside after dark. In Lourenço Marques, even mad dogs did-
n't venture abroad in the moonlight hours. Just Englishmen.

Brian pointed out some landmarks during the drive: the
Natural History Museum in the manner of a monumental
Turkish baths; the gothic-style cathedral, incongruously
fringed with palm trees; and the Tanduru Gardens, a munic-
ipal park which seemed well on its way to throwing off
colonial manicurings and reverting to a foliage free-for-all.
Eventually we arrived at the dockside and the car drew to a
halt. Brian instructed the driver to wait for us and we set off
on foot. Turning a corner into the narrow, chaotically cob-
bled Rua de Bagamoyo we at last found life aplenty, though
inevitably in such a place, at such a time, of the seriously
seedier sort.

★★★

The Bar Pombal has the trappings of a Harrogate tea shop,
but the patrons are red light revellers. The score-or-so tables
are covered with prim red and white checked tablecloths,
decked with jam-jars holding green and yellow plastic daisies
and wine bottle candlesticks crusted with cascading wax.

Saffron candle flames lollop fitfully in the *tabac-brune* fug, flicking glimmers and shadows across the faces of the barflies. They're a mongrel crowd: African tarts; pencil-moustached *piednoir* pimps; seamen of all sorts, Chinese, Greeks, Panamanians and Lascars; and young men in military uniform, blacks and whites, with their girlfriends, low-lifeing for an evening. But no-one is having fun. Brows are furrowed, mouths tightly-puckered, eyes wary and watchful. Over in the corner a tiny waif-like *chanteuse* sings a live soundtrack of slow, sad French songs.

Brian barks something at the waitress, who sets off for the bar.

'You speak Portuguese?' I ask.

'Just enough to get by in restaurants or buy a bus ticket,' he replies with an ill-at-ease laugh. He's a lousy liar. There's something sinister about Brian, but I can't fathom what it is. I feel relieved that I insisted on depositing my winnings in the hotel safe before we set off.

The waitress returns carrying a half-full bottle with a cork in the neck and two tumblers which she places on the table.

'You know *aguadente*?' asks Brian.

'No.'

'Well, you're in for an experience. Down the hatch in one, that's how to do it.'

We chime our glasses. I follow his instruction, slugging it Russian style. Cripes. My tongue scorches, my throat burns and it feels like there's a blow torch roaring in my sinuses. But then the flames subside into a rosy glow and I'm suffused by a feeling of warmth and well-being.

'You really Italian?' asks Brian. 'I mean, sometimes you sound almost like an Englishman.'

'You're very kind. I've been living in London recently.'

'Oh, I see. Lucky fellow. You know, it's the ordinary things I miss most. The sort of stuff you take for granted. I mean, a pint of bitter down the pub, fresh milk in a bottle on the doorstep, a British Railways bacon sandwich.' He titters nervously. 'How about you? What do you miss about home?'

'*Les enfants de la guerre, ne sont pas des enfants*,' sings the petite *chanteuse*. It's a minor key lament of devastating dismalness. Brian's nostalgia, the music's melancholia and the firewater vapours coalesce into a powerful assault on my *sang froid*. I'm remembering my friends, the club, lamb cutlets . . .

'Come on,' coaxes Brian. 'It's your turn now.'

I say nothing, my mind overwhelmed by reminiscences and regrets.

'Alright, put it this way,' he blunders on, 'what will be the first thing you do when you get back?'

My eyes are full of tears. I'm feeling horribly despondent. Hideously lonely. Cruelly unloved. I have to *tell* someone.

'I can never go back,' I mutter forlornly.

'Of course you can. Don't worry so much. Don't upset yourself so,' says Brian, now speaking in a gentle friendly voice. I draw consolation from his sympathy and my confession gushes out.

'I'm not who you think I am. I'm Lucky Lucan.'

'Who?'

'Lucky Lucan. You must have heard about me.'

'I haven't heard any news for months, old chap. No radio. It was eaten by termites a few weeks after arrival. And any newspaper that got through was snaffled by the natives and used to swat flies. You try reading *The Times* when its battered to ribbons and blotched with bluebottles.'

'I'm on the run.'

'A fugitive, eh? Who from?'

'The police. And an international terror gang too.'

'Tears are flooding down my cheeks. I'm weeping into my hands. Great heaving sobs that shake my whole frame.

Brian is watching me with a strange expression. He reaches

into his pocket and produces an aspirin bottle from which he shakes out two pills.

'Take these, they'll calm you down,' he says handing them to me with a comforting pat on the shoulder.

'I'll be fine,' I say, feeling embarrassed at making such a spectacle of myself.

'You're overwrought. Take the pills,' he orders. 'Trust me, I'm a doctor.'

I gobble the yellow capsules, washing them down with a swig of grog.

Almost immediately I feel tired. Really knackered. Brian stands up and walks towards the telephone. I try to follow, but I can't move a muscle. I'm totally rat-arsed. The drink is my first thought. But I haven't been drinking heavily. It has to be Brian's pills. The swine has slipped me a Mickey Finn . . .

***

My head was ringing when I awoke. It was a low rumble, rather like the noise made by the turbo-prop transport planes that took us to Germany when I was in the Guards. Then I noticed that the bed I was lying in was juddering slightly. I opened my eyes. I *was* in an aircraft, stretched-out across three seats covered by a coarse blanket for a cover. Raoul Matanzas was standing nearby watching me. He was wearing an olive-green military-style shirt, with insignia of some sort on the epaulettes.

'Good afternoon,' he said courteously with a gracious smile on his lips. A gentleman, as ever. 'I hope you have slept well. Allow me to introduce myself properly. Colonel Matanzas, Cuban Intelligence.' He extended an arm and we shook hands.

'I apologise for not consulting you about this trip, but you were unconscious. Once the good doctor informed us of your true identity we decided to act. My president is very keen to learn more about your activities in Africa. It is my pleasure to convey to you his invitation to visit our country. We arrive in Havana in three hours.'

'President who?'

'Fidel Castro, of course.'

Why on earth should Castro want to meet me, I wondered. All I could think of was that there was some connection with Carlos. After all, they were both revolutionary loonies.

'Suppose I decline his invitation to visit Cuba?'

'You are free to leave. The door's right there,' he said pointing at the aircraft's emergency exit. 'I don't want to take you all the way to Havana against your will.'

'Cuba sounds rather attractive, compared with the alternative.'

'I thought you wouldn't want to disappoint *el presidente*.'

'That chap Brian, he was working for you?'

'That's right,' replied Raoul with a look that said sorry for cheating. 'I knew there was something suspicious about you. I suspected you were a gun-runner, most likely supplying arms to our enemies the reactionary anti-Frelimo elements. So I hired the doctor to befriend you and find out about you. When he discovered your real identity he was instructed to dope you and to report back to me. So here you are.'

'I'm not a gun-runner, you're making a mistake. I'm just an ordinary businessman.' I sat up and reached into the pocket in the back of my trousers for my passport. It had gone.

'Looking for this?' said Colonel Matanzas, slapping it against the palm of his hand.

'Yes. Look inside. It says my occupation is businessman.'

'This is not your passport. We checked it out with our contacts in Jamaica. Toots du Maurier was a petty criminal who was killed by the Mafia six months ago.'

He paused. The thin smile on his lips indicated he was rather enjoying the game of cat and mouse. For sure. I was playing the part of the wee timorous beestie. 'You are not from Jamaica, you are Italian. You said so to Brian. When he told me that, the other things we had spoken about, the gambling and the guns, fitted into place. I knew we'd caught a big fish, but never guessed that we'd harpooned a whale. I guess you could say, "we got Lucky".'

So, the Cubans had 'Got Lucky'. But why bother? What on earth did Fidel Castro want with a runaway English Earl?

★★★

Over the years, I've met many people in positions of power, including quite a few heads of state, and it's my observation that most of them are mad. But Fidel Castro takes the biscuit. Frankly, his behaviour was so bizarre that he might have been from another planet. He probably is.

Upon arrival at the Palace of the Revolution, a disappointingly un-palatial slab run up in the 1950s by the pre-communist dictator Batista, Raoul and I were shown into an ante-room. A corpulent middle-aged man, wearing an open-necked brightly-coloured, tropical beach shirt was already in occupation. As we entered, he lowered his newspaper. Rising to his feet, he extended a hand.

'Hi,' he said in an English-sounding voice, though the pronunciation was somewhat guttural, 'I'm Bob Maxwell.'

At the time the name meant nothing to me, but I was astonished to come upon a fellow countryman under such circumstances, even the sort of chap Gussie and Boy would have instantly labelled a four-letter man.

'I am Colonel Matanzas and this gentleman is Senor Toots du Maurier,' said Raoul silkily.

Maxwell stared at me, his eyebrows hoist towards the heavens.

'Now that's a hell of a coincidence,' he boomed. 'Du Maurier used to be my name before I changed it to Maxwell. Actually, du Maurier wasn't my real name either. I took it from a fag packet during the war. I don't think they make the brand any more. But I could have chosen worse. Could have been Capstan or Camel!' He let out a great bellow of laughter. 'Speaking of camels, why do they call the camel the ship of the desert? Don't know? Because they're full of arab semen!'

He roared with laughter at his cringe-making joke and I confess that I found it impossible not to snigger, though mostly from embarrassment at the fellow's egregiousness. Raoul scowled disapprovingly. But Maxwell was encouraged by my half-hearted laugh.

'Say, do you know the one about the parking warden who gets shagged by a camel? No? Well, there's this parking warden walking along the street and she sees . . .'

At that moment a door opened and a young woman appeared dressed in olive-green military attire with insignia similar to Raoul's. She motioned us to follow her, leaving Maxwell in mid-flow. She was tall and trim and looked like she belonged on a catwalk. At the time I wondered how Castro kept his mind on his work or his hands to himself. Looking back, I guess she was probably his psychiatric nurse.

We were ushered into a spacious study. Sitting behind the desk at the far end of the room I saw the unmistakable bearded figure of *El Maximo Lider*, as the locals refer to Castro, puffing a big cigar. As instructed, I waited by the door while Raoul went over to the President and had some words with him, but all the time Castro's gaze was malevolently fixed on me.

When Raoul finished speaking, Castro cocked his little finger and beckoned me over. There was no invitation to take a seat and I found myself standing in front of his desk, like a schoolboy summoned to see the headmaster. He glared at me in silence while he took a long draw on his cigar and then blew the smoke into my face, his eyes beaming pure hate.

At last he spoke, in Spanish his words being translated by Miss Cuba in the military uniform.

'You are scum,' she announced in a cute cheer-leader voice with a sing-song Cuban-American accent.

I wondered whether she had got the translation quite right, but it soon became clear that the problem was more fundamental.

'You are a disgrace to the human race. You are less than a dog.'

I couldn't fathom why he should say such things. And why was everyone so down on dogs?

'How many brothels were there in Havana before the Revolution?' Castro demanded. What was going on here? A Cuban version of *Mastermind*?

I shrugged and held my peace, but my hackles were rising.

'And whores. How many whores before the Revolution?' ranted Castro angrily.

'How should I know?' I barked back. 'Bog Off!'

'You know the answers,' he screamed, pounding the table, 'because you and your kind turned my city and my country into a cesspool of prostitution, drugs, gambling and pornography. A playground for Yankee vermin. There were 11,500 prostitutes here in Havana when the Revolution came to power. All defiled by you!'

What had all this to do with me? I'd never set foot in Cuba before being kidnapped. And accusing me of hanky-panky with 11,500 of the local senoritas was ludicrous. I checked since, and even Don Juan only scored with 10,000.

'We read that you were dead,' continued Castro, now speaking calmly but with more than a hint of menace in his voice. 'That's what the capitalist media said. Lies as usual.

And now we discover you in Africa trying to corrupt our friends. Let me tell you, they have not thrown off one set of shackles to become slaves and tarts to trash like you. We will not let it happen. I will send troops to make sure it doesn't happen. You will see, Senor Luciano.'

What was he going on about now? I couldn't fathom it. He was barmy, that was my conclusion. Mad as a Martian. Potty as a Plutonian. Stark raving bloody bonkers. He couldn't even pronounce my name properly. Any moment now he'd start foaming at the mouth.

'You deserve to be shot,' announced Castro. 'But the Revolution is merciful. It has been decided that you will spend the rest of your miserable days toiling in the tobacco fields for the benefit of the masses. You will undergo Marxist-Leninist Corrective Re-education that will reveal to you the error of your criminal anti-social behaviour. Now get out of my sight, before I change my mind and order a firing squad.'

The aide shouted something at the pair of guards standing at the side of the room who hurried over and grabbed my arms. '*Vamoos*,' she ordered and I was bundled out of the presidential presence.

'Hey, du Maurier,' called Maxwell as we appeared in the waiting room. 'You free for a drink at the *Bar Floridita* tonight?'

'Afraid not,' I spluttered as I was frog-marched past him. 'I've just been given a life sentence for crimes against Cuban womanhood. I've never even been to Cuba before. I was kidnapped by Castro's agents. Help me. You're my only chance . . .'

***

Work in the tobacco fields wasn't half as bad as I'd expected. It was warm and sunny, and for me at that moment fresh air and physical exercise were just what the doctor ordered.

Admittedly, I'd have preferred to have been bob-sleighing in St Moritz or powerboat racing in the Bahamas, but they weren't on offer. Instead it was digging, ditching and weeding in amongst the tobacco plants. My accommodation was a charming rustic wooden hut with a bamboo roof covered in palm fronds, not unlike the sort of thing you pay through the nose to stay in at exclusive beach resorts. I derived some consolation from the thought that since it seemed to be my destiny to end up in a prison of some sort, a farm in Pinar Del Rio was a good deal more agreeable than a cell in Wormwood Scrubs and more peaceful than the basement in Earls Court. The grub wasn't bad, and there was plenty of home-brew rum.

The bloody bit, and it was absolutely stinking, were the compulsory lessons in Marxism-Leninism. I was put in a group of English speaking social outcasts, my class-mates comprising a dope-peddler, a shop-lifter and a smuggler. The method of instruction was distinctly Dickensian, parroting long passages from an abysmally translated Russian edition of *Das Kapital* published in 1947. It was brain-numbingly boring but insidiously effective. Soon even I was able to quote great swathes of incomprehensible wordage about historical materialism, the struggle of the masses, or whatever. I still can, but I don't find there's much call for it even at stag parties.

I like to think that the meaning of it all would have become clearer if I had got the end of the book. We were on page 282, around the half-way mark, when one day the class was interrupted by a prison guard and I was instructed to go with him. He led me round to the administration building, an imposing white-walled colonial hacienda. I was shown into an office where to my astonishment was the man I'd met in the ante-room at Castro's office.

'Hello, sunshine,' said Robert Maxwell grinning.

'What did they arrest you for,' I asked, my first thought being that he was joining our class.

'No-one's ever going to put me in jail,' he said, prophetically as it turned out. 'I've come for a chat about your future. I know all about your past.'

'Not all that Don Juan nonsense again,' I retorted, irritated anew by the memory of my meeting with Castro.

'No, the truth about your past. You're not really Toots du Maurier. You're Lucky Lucan, aren't you?'

I nodded, my mouth agape. Maxwell looked very pleased with himself. Like the proverbial cat that got the cream.

'How did you know?'

'I was curious about the coincidence of meeting another du Maurier, so I took Raoul Matanzas for a drink at the *Bar Floridita*. With a few *Mojitos* down the hatch, he revealed to me that your true identity was Lucky Luciano. That's who their agent in Lourenço Marques told them you were. That explains why the Cubans abducted you.'

This so-called explanation was clear as mud to me. 'Who's Lucky Luciano?' I asked.

'One of the big time Mafia bosses in the 1950s when the mob ran Havana as their playground. That's why they hold you personally responsible for the sleeze that went on at that time. But Lucky Luciano was an Italian-American and even with the best elocution teacher in the world there was no way he was going to be talking with a pronky accent like yours. So I figured that there had to be some sort of a mistake. And then I realised that there's only two little letters difference between Lucky Luciano and Lucky Lucan. I mean, lots of people could make a slip up like that.'

'So I'm here by mistake?'

'A case of mistaken identity.'

'Did you tell Colonel Matanzas? Can I go?'

'I did, but I'm afraid you're not a free man. You see, when

I explained who you *really* are they took the view that as an hereditary aristocrat you are a class enemy and in serious need of re-education. Moreover, apparently you entered the country illegally without a visa.'

'I was drugged and kidnapped.'

'There's no stamp in your passport, which is a serious offence. But under the circumstances, they've decided to reduce the sentence from life to twenty years.'

'What? So I'm stuck here for twenty years just because of my birth. That's outrageous. As a subject of Her Majesty, I'll demand to see the British Consul.'

'Not a smart move, under the circumstances, sunshine. But there might be another way out.'

'How?'

'I've just been talking to the governor of the prison, and he's prepared to do a deal. He'll set you free and pretend that you died of swamp fever in the hospital. Something like that. Matanzas and his people won't enquire closely. They'll be glad to be shot of you. The last thing he needs is for Castro to learn about his cock-up.'

'Why should the governor do that?'

'Oh, he won't just let you go. He'll swap you for a set of encyclopaedias.'

'Encyclopaedias?'

'He's very concerned about his children's education. Thinks it'll help them get on in life. He's a good father.'

'How on earth do I get hold of a set of encyclopaedias,' I wailed.

'That's where I may be of assistance,' said Maxwell smiling. 'You see, I'm a publisher and my company specialises in the publication of encyclopaedias. I'll provide the books, so long as you agree to work for me.'

'What?'

'I need someone like you. Someone who's prepared to tell

the President to "Bog Off!" Matanzas told me about that.
No-one's ever used those words to Castro's face before.
Secrecy is the other essential and I'm sure you're good at that.
You'll act as my personal envoy, reporting to me and no-one
else. No-one in my organisation will know of your existence.
Not even the family.'

'To do what?'

'To develop my *Leaders of the World* project.'

'What's that?'

'It's a series of autobiographies of the Presidents and Prime
Ministers of the world. US President Gerald Ford and
Harold Wilson, naturally, but also those who don't get a fair
press in the West. Todor Zhivkov of Bulgaria or Nicolae
Ceausescu of Romania, for example.'

'Does anyone want to read about them?'

'Of course not. But *they* want books about themselves
published in the West, and, one way or another, they'll pay
handsomely for the service. Neat, eh?'

'I suppose so,' I replied hesitantly. The point of publishing
books that had no readership eluded me, but Maxwell
seemed to know what he was doing.

'Good,' he said, beaming from ear to ear. 'I thought you'd
see it my way. The trouble about dealing with world leaders
is that they're busy men. Some of them keep you hanging
around for months on end trying to close a deal. That's why
I'm back in bloody Cuba! Now, I'm far too busy for all this
messing about. I've got a business to run. Which is where you
fit in, sunshine. Your job is to go round the globe confidentially chatting-up the Castros, the Ceausescus, the whoever,
getting them to sign up for the series. I'll provide the intro-
ductions, a new passport and pay your expenses. Any
questions?'

'If they're so busy, how do they find time to write an autobiography?'

'Of course they haven't got time. We hire a writer. Some reptile journalist, they're two-a-penny. That's the easy bit, the problem is pitching the proposal to them in the first place. And you're the man I need to do it.'

I was, to say the least, somewhat surprised at this turn of events. I knew nothing about publishing and regarded politicians in general as a form of life lower than bed-bugs. But the offer also had many attractions. The money. The passport. And the protection of working for a powerful patron.

'It's a deal,' I declared.

'Sign this,' said Maxwell handing me a piece of paper.

'What's this?'

'A contract of employment.'

'No it's not. It's a blank piece of paper.'

'Look, sunshine, I don't travel with a sodding contracts department in tow. I'm here alone and incognito. We'll fill in the details later. Now, sign the fucking form or I'll keep my encyclopaedias to myself.'

So I signed. It seemed an odd way to do business, but the alternative of two decades of Marxism-Leninism seemed worse than anything Maxwell could require me to do. Little did I know what lay in store.

4. Bongo In The Congo

'Who?'

'JEAN-BEDEL BOKASSA,' boomed Maxwell's deep sonorous voice down the 'phone. 'The president of the C.A.R.'

'The what?'

'The Central African Republic. What's the matter with you? Got your head up your bum?'

'Oh, *that* Bokassa,' I replied, endeavouring to maintain my dignity in the face of Maxwell's overbearing brutishness. In fact, I'd never heard of the man or the country.

'Take out a set of French language encyclopaedias as a gift from me. And make sure you give them to him yourself, I don't want them filched by some underling. Straight after the presentation, you call on the other ministers, tell them how much the boss likes the books and hand out order forms. They'll sign up for sets to keep up appearances. It always works.'

'I thought I was your special envoy, not an encyclopaedia salesman.'

'You'll do whatever I say, sunshine. You'll do it my way, or you'll find yourself behind bars before you can say "Bob's your uncle".' The phone went dead.

I went over to the bookcase and took down a volume from one of the sets of Pergamon encyclopaedias that had arrived one day from Maxwell without explanation. I'd assumed they were some sort of signing-on present. In fact, like everyone else who worked for him, I was required to flog them to all and sundry. The commissions were the only payments I received promptly from Maxwell – to spur me to sell more books.

Tome in hand, I strolled out on to the balcony and sat down in a deck chair. The morning was dewy fresh, but gentle and delicately perfumed with orange blossom. From my hillside apartment, the villas of Marbella and their gardens made a pretty patchwork of white and green stretching down to the brochure-blue sea.

Why Marbella? It was Maxwell's idea: handy for the international airport at Malaga; full of British ex-pats so I wouldn't attract attention; and, most important of all, Spain had no extradition treaty with Britain. What's more, property was cheap and I was able to afford a modest apartment with the money I'd removed from the flat in Earls Court when I escaped from Anwer and Carlos. A win on the local lottery boosted my bank balance, allowing me to live comfortably and quietly.

Known universally just as Johnny, I posed as a property developer who had recently gone bust in the great real-estate crash but had salted away enough loot in the fat years to settle on the Costa. Marbella was full of fugitives, people evading taxes, the law or reality and I merged readily into the milieu.

Nonetheless, I continued to take precautions against being recognised. I deliberately avoided the places where the ex-pats congregated: the golf clubs at Sotogrande or Los Monteros or the bars of Puerto Banus or Porto Pedro. And, of course, casinos were completely out of bounds. I kept my own company and when I went out I frequented the bars where the locals drank, away from the sea front. In fact, I became a bit of a regular in a couple of joints and acquired some genial native drinking partners.

I bought a canary-coloured Morgan cheap from a chap

who had grown homesick for Slough, an exceedingly rare complaint, I'd have thought. A bit flash for a fugitive? Not at all. Distinctly slumming it, amongst the Porsches, Mercedes SLs and Ferraris that litter that neck of the woods. And far from conspicuous; just another open-top, which meant I could disguise myself in my Biggles-style flying-headgear and goggles, a white silk scarf fluttering in the slipstream. Thus attired, I explored the hot spots of Estepona and Fuengirola, and the *Bar Sol y Sombra* in Ronda up in the hills became a favourite haunt.

As the months went by, the encounter with Maxwell seemed more and more like a distant dream. But then came the dreaded call and it was time for me to pay the piper.

The Central African Republic, I read in the encyclopaedia, is a land-locked former French colony bordered by Chad, Cameroon, Sudan, Zaire and the Congo. In other words, it's slap bang in the middle of darkest Africa, the south of the country being covered by equatorial rain forest. The climate is diabolical, six months of rainstorm alternating with six months of steambath. The population numbers some two million, most of whom are subsistence farmers living in dire poverty. Diamond mining is big business, but the economy is heavily dependent on handouts from France, bolstering its influence in the region.

That afternoon a package arrived from Maxwell by courier with a slab of photocopies of newspaper articles about President Bokassa gleaned from a cuttings library. The more I read, the more unsavoury he sounded. Starting as a corporal in the French colonial army, he had risen, by fair means and foul, to the rank of head of the army. He had come to power in 1965 when he had assumed the presidency by ousting his cousin. Welcomed at first as a relief from the previous repressive regime, Bokassa's conduct soon became both brutal and bonkers. In 1971 he celebrated Mother's Day by releasing all women prisoners, and executing men accused of murdering their mothers. The following year he decided to get tough on theft, ordering the cutting-off of ears for the first two offences, and a hand for the third. These mutilations having no effect on the crime wave, he personally supervised a beating of imprisoned thieves from which three died and 43 were maimed. A burglary at his residence got him really riled and selecting a number of prisoners at whim, he beat them to death, gouged out their eyes and put their mutilated bodies on public display.

My assignment was to sign-up this pocket-Hitler as a Maxwell author. Who on earth would want to read his auto-biography, I pondered. No-one that I could think of; well only Gussie and Boy who had a taste for that sort of thing. So why did Maxwell want to publish it? It was a mystery to me. But as Kipling might have put it, 'mine was not to reason why, mine was to do or die'.

***

I think it was W.C. Fields who quipped 'first prize: a week in Philadelphia; second prize: two weeks in Philadelphia'. If he had ever visited Bangui, the capital of the Central African Republic, he would surely have re-cast the destination.

Arriving by air on the Air Gabon flight from Libreville, you spot the mighty hazel-coloured Oubangui river cutting a swathe through the jungle long before you can make-out that there's a town perched on the bank. The first signs of human settlement are the top stories of the few high-rise buildings, but most of the city remains hidden, an urban undergrowth beneath the tall topical trees. As the plane banked and turned, beginning its descent to the airfield, the picture became clearer. I saw a criss-cross of laterite dirt tracks plied by pre-war lorries and buses, shambling shanty-town dwellings constructed from corrugated iron and plastic sheeting, goats and chickens scratching for food, and brightly-garmented children playing amongst them. All very picturesque, but a place I would have preferred to visit courtesy of *Whicker's World* from the comfort of my armchair rather than in person.

The airport terminal was hot and humid and I was greatly relieved to see a sign reading DU MAURIER, held aloft by a man in a chauffeur's hat. I strolled over and introduced myself, though keeping a watchful eye on the porters who were carrying my suitcase and two hefty wooden crates each containing seven volumes of a fourteen set encyclopaedia that was destined as an offering to President Bokassa. I had been warned by Maxwell of the notorious reputation of the natives for petty theft, and I was on my guard.

Like most chauffeurs, his appearance was thoroughly unremarkable: average height and build; an ordinary face; his attire neither strikingly smart nor scruffy. A regular Joe, which happened to be his name. But there was a special twinkle in his eye and his voice was full of fun. His command of the Queen's English was deplorable but he was fluent in jivetalk, having been schooled by soul-brother American missionaries from Harlem. He told me that he'd been sent by the president's office and had instructions to take me to the hotel mentioned by Maxwell. Thus reassured, I dismissed thoughts of being kidnapped with my precious cargo and entrusted myself into Joe's hands.

We travelled into town in a beat-up big black Mercedes that pounded along smooth as a panther, taking the ruts and pot-holes in its stride. During the drive, Joe gave me a run-down on the perils of tourism of Bangui. He had a catalogue of hair-raising tales of pick-pocketings, pilferings and snatchings, and even stories of sightseers being held up and left without a stitch of clothing in the middle of the jungle. Nodding towards the crates of encyclopaedias occupying the front passenger seat he remarked to me,

'Say man, why don't yer jus' stan' on der street corner hol-
lerin' "Christmas Has Come, Mother-fuckers"? Huh?'

Despite his obscure turn of phrase, I got his gist. I determined not to let the crates out of my sight until they were
safely delivered to the President.

Joe carried the crates into the hotel and I tipped him $5, a
rather generous gesture I thought. But instead of thanking
me, he told me that I owed him a further $10. I pointed out
that he was paid by the President, not by his guests. But I was
wrong. That wasn't the way things worked in the Central
African Republic. Public servants weren't paid for months or
even years and the way they survived was by charging for their
services or turning to crime. This, Joe explained, was the root
cause of the crime wave – impecunious policemen, judges,
doctors, nurses, teachers and civil servants trying to make
ends meet. He asked me to hurry-up because at that very
moment somebody was probably removing the tyres from his
car. Moved by his story, but more moved by the force of his
personality as he stood closely over me, I gave him a further
$20. Thanking me, he said that the hotel manager knew
where to find him when I had further need of his services.

My checking-in was conducted personally by the manager
who was effusive in his welcome. The book signed and the
passport details duly recorded, he handed me a sealed envelope bearing an official stamp. It contained a message from
the president's office informing me that His Excellency would
be out of town for ten days, but that he looked forward to seeing me on his return. I was well on my way to W.C. Field's
second prize. Damn it.

I explained to the manager that my crates contained gifts
for the President and asked him to store them in the hotel
safe. One of the porters measured them with a piece of string,
but when the results were reported to the manager he

declared that the hotel safe was far too small to accommodate even one of them. So I asked him to safeguard them for me. However he refused to take any responsibility for a gift for the President, explaining that his life wouldn't be worth living if something happened to them while in his custody. He was plainly terrified at the prospect of Bokassa's displeasure, so I let the matter drop. But that left me baby-sitting Maxwell's set of encyclopaedias until Bokassa returned to town.

Everywhere I went the encyclopaedias went too. When I went down to dinner the crates came with me, carried by Pierre and Emile who I hired for this purpose and who slept outside my bedroom door to ward off burglars. The encyclopaedias accompanied me to the bar, and out on to the terrace with its attractive view of the river. The eccentric white man with his two large crates were plainly something of a talking point amongst the rest of the clientele, and whenever I looked up I saw that all eyes were upon me.

Three days migrating between my bedroom and the hotel bar proved to be as much as I could take, and so I asked the manager to arrange for the services of Joe and some body-guards the following morning. Joe was there at the appointed hour, accompanied by four paratroopers dressed in camou-flage fatigues plus boots, belts and berets with sub-machine guns on straps slung over their broad shoulders. They stood to attention and saluted when I appeared. I asked Joe if this was an official escort? No, he replied, they were his cousins who, like everyone else, hadn't been paid for yonks and were available for freelance work. We settled on $100 a day for the whole team.

A Mercedes 300 is a big car, but sandwiched on the back seat between two black paratroopers built like refrigerators, each with a crate of encyclopaedias on his knees, it felt like a Mini. But at least the bloody books were safe, and I could enjoy my tour.

Bangui is a city of contrasts. Downtown towards the river it's Paris-on-the-equator. The main streets are elegant wide Champs Elysée-style avenues, shaded by enormous mango and flowering *flamboyant* trees, while the neat side-streets are lined with sedate, elegant colonial-era buildings occupied by government ministries. But away from the centre it's a bustling human ant-hill, especially the neighbourhood known as Km5 which teems with street-life up to every sort of mischief. There's street-vendors selling everything from antelope to zebra, and that's just the food stalls. I suggested that we might stop to stretch our legs and have a look round at the colourful scene. Perhaps get some lunch from one of the many street sellers. Joe dismissed this suggestion out of hand, saying the area was rife with thieves and street gangs and was much too dangerous for a white man, even if accompanied by four burly paratroopers with machine guns. But if I wanted some lunch, he knew just the place. And off we sped.

Astonishment mixed with a dash of fear was written across the faces of the clientele and staff upon the entrance of our little procession at the restaurant in the Avenue Boganda. Joe commanded a table for eight and it took no more than a couple of words from the waiter to persuade a group of diners to abandon their meals mid-mouthful and scuttle off the premises. Joe organised the *placement*, seating the crates at the head and foot of the table to everyone's amusement. He ordered the chef's special all round, a mixed grill of crocodile, monkey and wart hog. (Take it from me, wart hog tastes a bunch better than it sounds, but it's not a patch on lamb cutlet.) My guests tucked in like they hadn't eaten for a week, which according to Joe wasn't far from the truth. It didn't bother me – Maxwell was footing the expenses bill.

After lunch, washed down with half-a-dozen rounds of *Mocaf*, a local brew, we went sightseeing. By now I was firm friends with Joe and the boys, almost part of the family, and they were proudly eager to show me round their bailiwick. We visited the Boganda Museum, a remarkable treasure-trove of miscellaneous artefacts, ranging from Pygmy cooking utensils to Weimar Republic small change, housed in an old two-storey mansion that had formerly been a presidential palace. We saw the cathedral, the port, the central reference library, the Air France office and the Renault showroom. At each stop our entourage of a white man, chauffeur, four para-troopers and two big boxes proved a real show-stopper. There was some debate amongst the paratroopers about what to show me next, two favouring the car-hire office while the others pressed the case of a laundromat. The impasse was resolved by Joe's suggestion of a canoe trip on the Oubangui river, which met with universal approval, especially from yours truly, who has always enjoyed messing around in boats.

We needed three substantial canoes to accommodate our-selves, our cargo and the oarsmen. Our voyage aroused con-siderable curiosity amongst the ferrymen and lightermen of the Bangui waterfront and a dozen-or-so of them decided to tag along, so it was a veritable flotilla that made the journey to and from the *Ile des Serpents*, a popular place for picnics I was told. Henley Regatta sprang to mind, though I suspect that Squiffy Marchmain, fond as he is of blazers and Pimms, would not have recognised the likeness.

***

The following morning, I was awakened by a furious ham-mering on the door of the hotel bedroom.

'What's going on?' I called drowsily.

'It's Joe. Shift yer butt.'

I opened the door. Joe was standing there with two of the paratroopers, guns in hand and fingers on the triggers.

'What's the matter? I told you to come at 10 o'clock. It's only 7.30.'

'Quick boss. You get yer shit together smart now. Ain't no time to lose. Gotta git you an' dem boxes outta here. Word on de street is dat de *Cinq-a-Onze* is on der way to heist you'se property. Dey heard about our outin' yesterday, and figure dat anythin' dat's worth dat much protection hastabe worth stealin'.'

'The *who*?'

'The *Cinq-a-Onze*. It's a gang of grade school teachers who ain't seen der money, like everyone else. Man, they'se de meanest. You don't fuck with de *Cinq-a-Onze*, man.'

'Where are we going?'

'I'se gonna' drive yer outta town to Bimbo where we'll find a guide to take yer to de Pygmies. Dey'll hide yer till de heat's off.'

'Hide amongst Pygmies? Don't you think I'll be just a little conspicuous? I'm six foot three inches.'

'In de rain forest, dumb-ass. No-one's gonna find yer dere if you'se with de Pygmies. Stop arguin' and git yer shit together.'

I opened my suitcase and started to pack. Mystifyingly, I could find only one of my brown broques and several of my shirts seemed to be missing. So were most of my handkerchiefs, half my socks and the trousers of my beige safari suit. I started to search for the missing items, but Joe was getting increasingly agitated. Then he exploded and ordered me to stop tossing about and leave all my stuff behind. We fled downstairs and joined the boys and the boxes of encyclopaedias in the Mercedes.

'What time do the banks open in Bangui?' I asked as we sped away.

'Seven o'clock. You'se short of money?'

'No I was thinking of depositing the boxes at a bank for safe-keeping while I'm out of town. I suspect they may be a bit of a damn nuisance in a Pygmy encampment in the equatorial rain forest.'

'Handy for sittin' on roun' de campfire,' suggested Joe practically.

'But hell to carry. Pull up over there at that bank,' I said pointing at a large white building.

The manager at the Banque de Brazzaville couldn't have been more accommodating. He declared himself delighted to look after my goods while I was out of town, though, of course, there would be a modest, as he put it, storage charge that had to be paid up front. Handing over an outrageous sum, we sped out of town for Pygmy country.

★★★

How many other members of the House of Lords have spent a week with a tribe of Pygmies deep in the equatorial rain forest? None, I'll wager. Mind you, these days some of the denizens of the bench of bishops are dark horses. But even the lords spiritual could learn a lesson or two about the meaning of life from these simple people who are completely at one with nature and the universe.

The Pygmies' hospitality was simply second-nature. I was cordially welcomed and led off to the guest hut, a domed structure made from a frame of bent saplings covered by large leaves. It looked painfully small for a man of my size, and my hosts plainly had the same thought since an awful brou-ha-ha blew up amongst them as we stood at the threshold. The problem was resolved by the construction of an identical edifice adjacent so that I could lie fully stretched out with half my body in each hut. The resemblance of my habitation to a pair of breasts caused hilarity amongst the Pygmies. I could tell whenever they were talking about me because they made a certain not very subtle gesture with cupped hands and everyone broke into gales of laughter. *O sancta simplicitas.*

Armed with a rifle borrowed from Joe, I joined the men on

their hunting expeditions. Mostly the bag was parrots and monkeys, but sometimes they got an antelope or a buffalo. We also saw a lowland gorilla, a creature that brought to mind Squiffy Marchmain that night at the Berkeley Square Fancy Dress Ball when he played an absolutely stonking prank with a banana on one of the young Cholmondeley girls.

One day we went honey gathering, a bees nest being spotted in a tree. Without a second thought, one of the young men shimmied up a tall palm bare-footed. Meanwhile the others prepared a bundle of smouldering leaves that he hauled up and used to smoke out the bees. Then he removed the honey combs with his bare hands. Now that's what I call intrepid. I'd like to see the Bishop of Liverpool do likewise.

At night we sat around the camp fire eating, drinking, singing and dancing. My Pygmy chums were particularly fond of *ngbako*, a sort of schnapps made from manioc root. Unfortunately its after-effect was a hangover that was far from Pygmy-sized. In the evenings, I was unable to participate usefully in the festivities until I had learned to master the bongo drums. Every evening I was given tuition by the tribe's leading bongo drummer and my playing advanced by leaps and bounds. In fact, much to my surprise, I discovered I was, as they say, a natural.

In return for the bongo lessons, I tutored the whole tribe in Scottish country dancing. The equatorial rain forest is not an ideal space for a Duke of Perth or the Reel of the 51st Division, but the Pygmies are a plucky people and gave a sporting account of themselves. They adored my imitations of the bagpipes, produced by an adenoidal humming in the nasal passages. I had them in stitches every evening and they implored me to stay and offered to make me an elder of the tribe. Tempting as I found the invitation, I'd taken Mr Maxwell's shilling and felt honour-bound to do my duty. I also have to confess that after a week of eating monkey and parrot, lamb cutlets were much on my mind. So, with a heavy heart, I bid farewell to my diminutive muckers.

★★★

Joe was there to meet me, as arranged, when I got to Bimbo. During the drive back to Bangui he related the mayhem caused by the *Cinq-a-Onze* gang in their frenzied search for me and my boxes. But all was quiet now. Bokassa was back and so was the presidential guard and even the primary school teacher desperadoes were wary of falling foul of them.

Our first stop in Bangui was the hotel where I intended to have a bath, a shave and to change my clothes, a week in the rain forest having taken a heavy toll of my blazer, roll-necked shirt, jeans and deck shoes; truth-be-told, I was so dishevelled, I looked like Robinson Crusoe. I assumed that it was my appearance that prompted the manager to start gibbering like his home was in a tree when I stepped into the lobby. When I saw my room I realised the real reason. It was a shambles. The *Cinq-a-Onze* goons had given it a more-than-thorough going over, even gutting the mattress of its stuffing and slashing the pillows. The whole mess was covered in a fine film of feathers that stirred and settled as I searched for my possessions. I found a few items of my clothes, but most had disappeared, as had my radio, my washbag, and even the suitcase itself.

It was as I was surveying the scene of devastation that the manager re-appeared and handed me an envelope which had just been delivered by motorbike courier. It was a summons to go immediately to the presidential residence for an audience with Bokassa. I said that I couldn't possibly visit the President wearing rags and demanded my clothes. The manager retorted that he'd see what could be done, but that it would be very dangerous to keep Bokassa waiting. Joe earnestly agreed. A few minutes later a chamber maid appeared clutching a collection of clothing that she thrust into my arms.

'You change super quick and go bugger-off,' said the manager, 'or else we all in big trouble.'

'Whose clothes are these?' I demanded, recognising my own safari suit trousers, but not the garish blue and pink blazer, the saffron-coloured shirt or the un-matching brace of shoes.

'Lost property,' explained the manager. 'Just get a move on.'

I did as I was told. Glancing at myself in the mirror I saw a figure who would have been at home on the boards in an Edwardian music hall. The final touch was an old-Etonian tie; I hope my *alma mater* will forgive the affront of the indignity of that ensemble.

En route for the presidential residence, we called at the Banque de Brazzaville to collect the precious encyclopaedias. The manager, looking even more sheepish than his counterpart at the hotel, explained that they had been taken away by soldiers at gun point. He was very sorry but there was nothing he could do. I told him that the boxes were a gift for Bokassa and that this was a very serious matter. He let out a horrible howl and started to cry and wail dropping to his knees shaking like a leaf and kissing my shoes, the brogue lace-up on my right foot and the wedge-fronted slip-on on my left. What was I to do? I promised him that I would say nothing of the matter to the President, so long as he returned my down-payment for his custody services with a hefty dollop of interest. I've never seen a bank manager so eager to press money into my hands, before or since.

***

From everything I'd read an heard about Jean-Bedel Bokassa

I was expecting a cold psychopathic ogre. But the man who met at the door of his official residence, smiling and warmly shaking my hand, was a genial buffer. He was short in stature with a fit, sinewy physique. His skin was as dark as the wood of the ebony trees growing in the nearby rain forest and had the lustre of polished leather, highlights glinting on his tall forehead, prominent cheekbones and broad, hump-back nose. His upper lip sported a neatly trimmed Sandhurst-style moustache. There were premature flecks of grey in his cropped crinkly hair; the wages of high-office, I reflected.

Apologising profusely for his recent absence from Bangui, he led me over to an elegant Louis XVI suite of furniture and we sat down in armchairs facing each other.

My attention was caught by the painting on the wall behind him. It was a copy of David's famous equestrian portrait of Napoleon crossing the Alps that hangs in the Louvre. Bokassa turned, following my gaze to the picture.

'I was born a Frenchman, you know, and served in the French army. Like all Frenchman, I am a great admirer of Bonaparte,' he said in French, his words being translated for me by a smartly-suited aide.

'He was a very great man. A great leader,' I replied. 'Of course, you are the Napoleon of the Central African Republic.' I added, creepily, seeking to ingratiate myself with my words, being unable to do it as intended by presenting him with the votive set of encyclopaedias.

A radiant smile formed on his features. 'Thank you Monsieur du Maurier. You speak flatteringly, but wisely. Now tell me, what are you doing here in Bangui?'

'I'm here as the special envoy of Mr Robert Maxwell, the leading international publisher.'

'To sell encyclopaedias?'

'No, no. Mr Maxwell wants to publish your auto-biography.'

Bokassa gazed at me bewilderedly. 'I haven't written an autobiography.'

'That's not a problem.'

'No?'

'We'll arrange for a journalist to write it for you.'

'Journalists!' He spat the word. 'I hate journalists. They write nothing but lies about me. Fortunately, Priscilla isn't picky about her food.'

'She eats journalists?' I gasped, horrified at hearing the rumours of cannibalism in Bokassa's household confirmed by his own mouth.

'She'll eat anyone. Even you, Monsieur du Maurier,' he replied menacingly. It was then that I noticed his eyes. I remembered someone saying that the eyes are the windows on a man's soul. Bokassa's were cerise dots in nicotine-coloured *coulis*, like bloodstains on bandages.

'You must pay her a visit on your way out,' he said smiling. 'She lives in the swimming pool.'

'In the swimming pool?'

'In the water.'

'In the water?'

'Why do you repeat my words?' he asked irritably. 'That is normal for a crocodile.'

'Let me explain Mr Maxwell's project,' I said, deciding to move on to a safer subject. 'He's producing a collection of the autobiographies of world leaders who don't get a fair hearing in the West. Fidel Castro, Leonid Breshnev and Nicolai Ceausescu, for example, are being approached to join the series. Maxwell thought that you too might like to tell your story.'

'That's an interesting idea,' said Bokassa pensively. We sat in silence while he reflected on the proposal, gazing at me all the while. I sensed him scrutinising me and felt more than a little uneasy in my ill-assorted and ill-fitting clothes.

'I can tell from your appearance that you are not a rich man, Monsieur du Maurier. Why does Monsieur Maxwell send an encyclopaedia salesman to speak to me?'

'I'm not an encyclopaedia salesman,' I protested. 'I am his special envoy.'

'Then why did you come to Bangui with a set of encyclopaedias? For reference purposes?'

How on earth did he know about the books, I pondered.

'They were intended as a gift for you from Mr Maxwell. But I lost them while I was waiting for your return. I also lost all my luggage. These clothes are borrowed from the hotel.'

'Well, I'm happy to be able to inform you that the books arrived safe and sound. They're over there on the bookshelves.' I looked round and saw 14 large red volumes bound in Morocco leather.

'How did they get here?' I asked in astonishment.

'My agents heard about the trouble you took to guard the boxes and assumed that they must contain something of great value. When it was learned that you had left town abandoning them, it was decided to take them into safe custody.'

'I left them in a bank for safe-keeping,' I protested.

'Monsieur du Maurier, theft is an unfortunate fact of life in my country. I have done my best to eradicate it, but it continues to be all too commonplace. I assure you that they are much more secure here. We don't have burglaries here, not any more. I'm afraid that my agents were very disappointed to find that the boxes contained only books. You see, they were hoping for diamonds or gold. Now that I know that they were intended for me, I must express my gratitude for your generous gift.'

'I'm glad they please you. Mr Maxwell will be very happy,' I said, feeling mightily relieved to be able to report back to Maxwell that his precious books had arrived safe and sound, despite taking a rather circuitous route. I found my gaze resting again on David's portrait of Napoleon in order to avoid Bokassa's eyes.

'You are interested in Napoleon?' he enquired.

'Yes. Very much so.' It seemed to be the right thing to say.

'Come with me please. I have something I would like to show you.'

Bokassa rose and led the way out of the room, followed by myself and the aide. Stopping before a door, he reached into his pocket for the key and unlocked it. We stepped inside.

It was an amazing sight. I had heard of such places, but had never seen one before. Every inch of the walls was covered by prints and paintings of Napoleon Bonaparte at various stages of his life, there were glass cabinets full of artefacts associated with him, as well as busts, banners, swords, pistols, a hat, a shoe and even an earthenware jar purporting to contain his toenail clippings. Bokassa was a Napoleon nutter!

He stood there proudly looking-on in silence while I perused the collection, purring 'marvellous' or 'wonderful' every few paces in the hope of humouring him enough to make sure of getting out alive.

'You like my collection?' he asked.

'It's very impressive,' I replied.

'I have been thinking about Monsieur Maxwell's proposal. I agree, but on one condition.'

'What's that?'

'I will tell you later, but first I have something else to show you that will help you understand.'

Beckoning for me to follow, he went over to the door on the far side of the room. This time there were two locks to turn. What on earth lay beyond, I wondered? His torture chamber? A charnel house? The pit and the pendulum? No, it was something much more awesome. Bokassa's *sanctum sanctorum* was a shrine to a King – the King of Rock 'n' Roll, Elvis Presley.

I wandered round the room thunderstruck. The walls were plastered with pictures of Elvis, like a teenager's bedroom. There were photographs of him as a child, an adolescent, in the US Army, in concert as a young man and as a more mature performer; posters promoting films called *Fun in Acapulco, Girls! Girls! Girls!*, *It Happened At The World's Fair* and *Jailhouse Rock*; a boxer's jock-strap, helpfully captioned, as were the others, from *Kid Galahad*; a garland of paper flowers featured in *Blue Hawaii*; the lumberjack shirt worn in *Kissin' Cousins*; the sunglasses from *Viva Las Vegas*; the guitar that he played on *Louisiana Hayride* in 1957; and the belt that held his trousers up in *Lovin' You*. Even the carpet had an Elvis Presley monogram motif.

'Amazing, absolutely amazing,' I heard myself saying in an awe-struck voice as I stared at the preposterous collection of tat. So the President of the Central African Republic, besides being a mass murderer and diamond thief, had a Napoleon complex, an Elvis obsession and a very large crocodile called Priscilla. Maybe his biography wouldn't be such a dull read after all.

Bokassa was grinning, pleased by my reaction. 'You too are a collector?' he enquired.

'Just a fan. I'm familiar with his music,' I blurted, recalling the days in the flat in Earls Court with Anwer. 'Tell me, how did you put together your remarkable collections?'

'My ambassadors have instructions to buy such treasures for our national museum. Do not misunderstand, they are not my personal collections, they belong to the people. I'm just looking after them while they are assembled.'

Retracing our steps into the Napoleon room, Bokassa halted in front of a large print captioned, 'Napoleon Bonaparte, crowning himself in the Cathedral of Notre Dame, Paris, 2nd December 1804'. And there he was, standing in front of the altar looking like Liberarce in a long robe with a fur collar placing an enormous crown on his head.

'Did you know that Napoleon made himself Emperor of France and established his family as the hereditary ruling dynasty?'

'I think we learned about it at school,' I replied evasively. As an hereditary peer of the *ancien regime*, it was just the sort of *arriviste* behaviour of which I thoroughly disapproved, but I deemed it prudent to keep my thoughts to myself.

'I intend to follow his example,' said Bokassa.

'Become Emperor?'

'Yes.'

'You think the French will go along with that?'

'Not of France. Of my country.'

'But this is a republic – it's called the Central African Republic.'

'So was France, until Napoleon made it an empire. I shall do the same for my people. Our country will become the Central African Empire.'

'Are you sure your people want to live in an empire?'

'Who would want to live in a republic, if they could live in an empire?'

I couldn't think of an answer to that.

'We will have massive celebrations to mark the occasion,' continued Bokassa, 'even more magnificent than Napoleon's. I have been reading a book about his coronation. There were salvoes of canon, *flambeaux*, fireworks, feasts, an enormous procession, dancing in the streets. We will have all this and more.'

'Won't it be hideously expensive? How can a poor country afford such celebrations?'

'Oh we won't be paying. The French will pick up the bill. We'll just have a damn good party,' snapped Bokassa irritably. He sounded impatient, as if my questions were preventing him from getting to the point.

'Monsieur du Maurier, I have a proposal to put to you. I will agree to Monsieur Maxwell's book, on condition that you help me.'

'What do you have in mind?' I said sheepishly, expecting some grisly assignment.

'I want you to undertake a very delicate overseas mission. I want you to persuade Elvis Presley to sing at my coronation. Will you do this for me?'

Elvis Presley? In Bangui? The turmoil in my mind as I grappled with the implications of his request must have registered on my face. Bokassa's expression darkened into a frown.

'He never leaves America,' I said, recalling what Anwer had told me back in the flat in Earls Court. 'These days he only ever performs in Las Vegas.'

I was desperate to find a way of scotching this silly scheme that could only end in a rebuff, for which I would be blamed.

'Not for a king's ransom?' replied Bokassa. 'Money is no problem. The French are paying for everything.'

Not for all the tea in China I wanted to say, but that wasn't the way one talked to tyrants like Bokassa if one preferred not to become Priscilla's elevenses. I decided to try a different tack.

'I'm afraid that I've got an awful lot of work to do for Mr Maxwell. I won't have time to negotiate with Elvis as well.'

'Then Monsieur Maxwell will not be enjoying your services,' said Bokassa icily. 'I understand that you imported a set of encyclopaedias into the country without paying customs duty. That is a very serious offence, carrying a ten year jail sentence. Of course, in some circumstances a presidential pardon is possible. But that is your only hope.'

I realised I was playing on a pretty sticky wicket. Plainly Bokassa wasn't going to take *no* for an answer. There was also

Maxwell to consider. How would he react if I made a bish of my first job for him? Nastily, I suspected.

'If I talk to Elvis Presley, you will grant a presidential pardon and co-operate with Maxwell's book?' I asked.

'If you persuade Elvis to sing at my coronation, I will do much more. I will give you a fistful of diamonds. I will make you a peer of the Central African Empire. How about an earldom? Earl of Bimbo sounds good, don't you think?'

'Excellent,' I replied jauntily, rather relishing the thought of the faces at Debretts. The other reason for my changed humour was that I had just had an idea that might allow me to pull off this absurd assignment – an assignment I had to complete for Maxwell as well.

'I agree to your proposal,' I said, 'but you'll have to give me something rather special to persuade Elvis.'

'Anything you want. My aide will see to it. Our talk is over now. I have an appointment at the prison. Your diplomatic credentials and whatever else it is you need will be delivered to your hotel tomorrow, along with an airline ticket and money to cover your expenses. One last thing, you must get some new clothes. Your attire may be acceptable to Monsieur Maxwell, but I won't have my ambassadors looking like scarecrows. *A bientôt*, Monsieur du Maurier. I look forward to our next meeting on your return from America.'

5. *Ambassador To Elvis*

Elvis. The biggest thing that ever happened to Memphis, Tennessee. Probably the only thing. They don't let you forget it. There's a statue on Main Street. A museum. A highway called Elvis Presley Boulevard. Street signs in the shape of a guitar. And Graceland; then his home, now his mausoleum. At last I understood how Anwer had come up with the code-name, Commando Graceland.

The Heartbreak Motel off Interstate 55 was my bivouac. It wasn't like anything I recognised as an hotel, being a collection of wooden mobile cabins with a bed and TV, basin and loo, alongside a concrete car dock. The wallpaper was a repeat pattern picturing Elvis strumming a guitar floating in a sea of minims and semi-quavers. His face featured on the bedside plastic ashtray and was even stencilled on the mirror in the bathroom. There was no escaping Memphis's favourite son.

I picked up the 'phone and called Graceland.

'Graceland. This is Mary-Lou. How may I help you?'

'I am the ambassador of the Central African Republic. I want to arrange a meeting with Mr Presley.'

'You'll have to speak with Stud.'

'Stud?'

'It's short for Studebaker, his father's favourite automobile marque,' she said mechanically as though she had run through the routine a million times before. 'He's Mr Presley's acting chief of staff. Putting you through. Have a nice day.'

'Hi, Stud here,' said a man's voice with a hill-billy twang.

'Good morning. My name is du Maurier. I am Ambassador Plenipotentiary of the President of the Central African Republic. I have a decoration to bestow on Mr Presley and would like to make arrangements for the presentation.'

Silence.

'Come again?' said Stud suspiciously.

'I want to meet Mr Presley to give him an honour from the Central African Republic. It's a country in Africa. Central Africa.'

'Jeeeez,' hissed Stud, his breath whistling through his teeth. 'Listen mister and listen good, we get all kinds of crazies calling up here, but I never heard that one before. Anyway Elvis ain't doin' no meetings at the moment.'

'Now, don't be hasty. Of course, I will bring my diplomatic credentials for your perusal.'

'Perusal? Ain't no perusal here. Just a Doberman to see off the sickies, likes of you.'

'Why not take a look?'

'At what? I don't wanna look at nothin' of yours, mister. Just skedaddle, ya hear me?'

'Want to make $5,000 this afternoon?'

'You for real?'

'Judge for yourself. I'll be round in half-an-hour. Tell your security guards to admit Ambassador du Maurier, and lock up the dog.'

'OK.'

I checked my appearance in the mirror. I looked the very picture of a suave cosmopolitan diplomat in a charcoal worsted three-piece, crisp white shirt and sober silk tie. In fact, I looked myself again. Dash, it felt good to be wearing proper togs after all that poncy fancy dress. There was a spring in my step as I snatched up my smart peccary executive briefcase and beetled out to the gleaming big black Dodge parked outside.

***

I pulled up round the back of the house as instructed by the guard at the gate. Stud, predictably attired in jeans and a lumberjack shirt, was waiting by the door. He was a big man built like a bouncer. He had the brain-size of a bouncer too. But even bouncers understand money.

'What's all this about?' said Stud, not with hostility but with bewilderment. I handed him an envelope. I smiled.

'Count it.'

He did. He frowned.

'You said $5,000. I make it $2,500.'

'You get the rest after I see Elvis.'

'Like I said, he ain't doin' interviews.'

'This isn't an interview. It's an official presentation. Elvis collects police badges, right?'

Stud nodded affirmatively, jaws ajar.

'Well, as President Bokassa's Ambassador Plenipotentiary I am empowered to make him honorary Chief of Police of Bangui, capital of the Central African Republic. Take a look.'

I opened the briefcase on the bonnet of the car. Inside was a large silver sheriff's star, like in the Westerns, bearing the words:

ELVIS PRESLEY
Chef du Police
Bangui, CAR

picked out in diamonds. Gosh it was gucky.

'Them's real diamonds?' asked Stud sceptically.

'Sure.'

'Jeez. How much is it worth?'

'It's priceless. It's the only one in the world. And now it's time to give it to Elvis. You wouldn't want me to walk away

with it would you? I don't think Elvis would be very pleased
when he found out.'

'Me neither. You'd betta come in. He's watchin' TV. But
I'm warnin' ya, this ain't one of his good days.'

***

I follow him up the short flight of steps that leads to a
small lobby, past the kitchen where he calls 'Hi' to a couple
of women cooks, then down a flight of steps into the basement and we're in the TV room. The absence of daylight is
compensated for by the mirrors that cover the ceiling and
much of the walls, complicatedly reflecting and multiplying
the beams of the overhead spots. The carpet and cushions
are sherbet-coloured and the velour-covered sofa is corn-
flower. Down the far end are three TVs set in the wall
babbling simultaneously. Two are showing football games
while the one in the middle is playing some crummy sit-
com.

Slumped on a sofa, feet up on a mirror-tiled coffee table, is
a 22 stone sweaty slob horsing a hamburger while he stares at
the screens. Where's Elvis I wonder?

"Scuse us El,' says Stud, 'you'se got a visitor.' My God, is
that Elvis the Pelvis? What has happened to the sleek Adonis
in the photographs in Bokassa's shrine? To the King of Rock
'n' Roll featured on Anwer's album cover?

'I told you, no visitors,' says the tub of lard.

'Aww, but this guy's come all the way from Africa. An' he's
got somethin' real pretty for ya. Somethin' you'se really
gonna like. Somethin' for your collection of police badges. A
real special one too.'

'Not as special as the badge President Nixon gave me,' said
Elvis, his words slurring into one another.

'Sure El, not as special as that,' said Stud with a hint of
exasperation in his voice, as if going over familiar ground with

a small child, 'but pretty special even so. Ya oughta take a look.'

'I'm hungry. I want a couple of cheeseburgers, some fries and a banana split.'

'Aww El, y'know ya don't oughta eat that junk. You'se meant to be dietin', goddamn it. Dr Nick is gonna go hog-wild when he realises ya bin on one of your eatin' binges. Gonna give me grief an' all. It just ain't fair.'

Elvis isn't listening. He's gazing at the TVs with heavy-lidded eyes, his face a vacant lot.

'Aww shuck,' exclaims Stud and heads off towards the kitchen to pass on the order. I watch Elvis while he's gone. Can this vast beached whale really be the legendary King of Rock 'n' Roll?

'That's about as funny as a turd in a punch bowl,' growls Elvis malevolently at the TV. He reaches into a pocket of the white karate kimono he's wearing and brings out a gun. It's not a standard issue model. This Colt .45 has a chrome muzzle and a special turquoise enamelled handle. He raises it slowly, aims and fires. I wince at the assault on my eardrums. The television shatters and falls silent. So Anwer was right about Elvis's habit of shooting-out TV sets. I pray that he's also right about his interest in police badges.

'What's the hell's goin' on?' demands Stud, charging into the room.

'Seems to be somethin' wrong with the TV,' says Elvis giggling. He sounds more animated now, as if the gunshot has woken him up. 'Stud, go git one that works good.'

'Aww, not again,' says Stud wearily. 'In a minute, OK? But first ya gotta talk with this guy here. He got a gift for ya.'

'A gift? For me?' says Elvis with childlike alertness. He seems to have forgotten about the conversation about me a minute-or-so before. Stud motions for me to do my stuff. I step forward. Elvis puts the gun back in his pocket, which takes a weight off my mind.

'Mr Presley, I am Ambassador Plenipotentiary of President Jean-Bedel Bokassa of the Central African Republic. I have been instructed by him to present you with a badge and certificate making you honorary Chief of Police of Bangui, the capital of his country.'

I open the box containing the badge, taking care to tilt it up and down so that the diamonds catch the spotlight and sparkle in his eyes. A smile passes across his blubbery baby-like features. He extends an arm and I pass it over.

'That's real nice. That's the best of the whole collection. Even Dick Nixon's ain't got no sparklers. Which force did you say?'

'Bangui.'

'Where's that? Sounds like California.'

'It's in Africa,' says Stud.

'Africa? In Georgia, right?'

'That's Atlanta, boss. Africa ain't no place in America,' adding by way of elucidation, 'ya know, it's where the coons come from, way back when.'

Elvis looks puzzled, but it passes and he resumes playing with his new toy. However, I'm heartened by Elvis's grasp of geography; after all, once he's on the plane what's the difference between Vegas and Bangui?

'I wanna give you somethin' for journeyin' all this way,' says Elvis. He snaps his fingers and Stud comes over with a photograph of the King. He's lithe, lean and handsome, like in a different life.

'What's the name?' he asks, pen in hand.

'Make it to "Lucky", that's my nickname,' I reply. 'To Lucky, from Elvis' he writes and then hands it over with a beatific smile. The man is high as a kite. Time to persuade him to come to Bangui.

'President Bokassa is having a party and has sent me to

invite you. A very special sort of party. It's his coronation. That means he wears a crown and becomes an emperor. He thought that you, the King of Rock 'n' Roll, ought to be there. He's a big fan of your music.'

'A party? I dig parties. Was a time we had plenty of parties right here, at the house. Don't seem to happen no more.'

'The coronation's scheduled for December. Can you come?'

'I damn sure can.'

'And do you think you might sing a couple of songs. Just for fun, you know.'

'Sure thing. Sounds wild.'

'Aww El, don't mess with the guy,' interjects Stud. 'You know the Colonel ain't gonna go along with that.'

'Who's the Colonel?' I ask.

'Colonel Parker, Elvis's manager. He ain't never let him perform overseas before. Can't imagine it'll be any different this time.'

'That's where you're damned wrong,' growls Elvis. 'If I wanna go partying, I'll go partying. If I wanna have a party, I'll have a party. I'm mad as a peach orchard boar with bein' forever told "don't do this", "don't do that". An' I tell you what, I'm gonna have a party of my own tonite.'

'You'se is?' says Stud, looking harassed and horrified.

'I sure am. In the den. It's gonna be like the old days. So quit moaning' and git organisin', mister.'

'I wasn't around here in them times. What's you want me to do?'

'Sometimes Stud, you'se as dumb as a prairie dog's fart. Wine, women and song, Stud. Get the guys together.'

'The guys?'

'Yeah, the guys. My ol' buddies. This guy's comin' too, ain't ya?'

'Well . . . errr . . .' I mumble, feeling distinctly sheepish about the prospect of partying Presley-style.

'Damn right, you are,' says Elvis, 'else I ain't comin' to your party.'

'I'm delighted to accept your invitation,' I reply, wondering what I'm letting myself in for.

'That's good. Boy are we gonna have fun tonite. You know they used to call us the Memphis Mafia, me and the guys,' Elvis says to me in a confidential tone and winks. He seems to have taken to me.

'But the guys have gone, El,' moans Stud. 'You and yer dad, ya fired 'em all.'

'Don't give me that bullshit. I want them here tonite. Go git 'em you lazy jackass. I want to party tonite, you dig?'

'Sure thing, El,' says Stud, rolling his eyes to the heavens.

Plainly it's no picnic, being chief of staff to the King of Rock 'n' Roll.

★★★

I arrived back at Graceland at about 10 o'clock, as instructed by Stud. Slowing as I passed the graffiti covered 'wall of love', I nosed the Dodge through the gaggle of girls waiting even at that hour for a glimpse of the King.

Up at the house a spruce young man in a bell-boy tunic opened the driver's door for me. Leaving him to valet-park the car, I crunched across the gravel to the tall white-pillared portico and walked through the open front door. Lifting a Scotch-on-the-rocks off the platter proferred by a waiter, I followed his directions to the den where the party was taking place.

The den was cosy and dark, lit only by a couple of table lamps with subdued citrus shades and the flickering glow from the large TV that scattered shadows around the room. Peering into the dimness, I made out that the walls were panelled with pine planks, like a super-size sauna, while at the far end there was a rock face with water pitter-pattering from stone to stone into a pool at the bottom. Strands of creeper rooted in crevasses cascaded floorwards into a lushly planted indoor flowerbed. The floor was carpeted in moss-green shag pile. The ceiling too. As the Reverend McVitie once pronounced, it is a short step from avant-garde to absurd.

A jungle motif ran through the fittings and ornaments: there were miniatures of lions and tigers, monkeys and elephants; a mirror in a frame decorated with bird feathers; an antelope skull with writhing horns; nylon pelt on the bar stools; and the furniture featured the sort of native carving usually reserved for totem poles. The keynote item, was a king-size semi-circular armchair covered in fake fur, the looming headrest taking the form of a face, probably an owl's but reminding me of Squiffy Marchmain the time we were served mulled sweet cider. And there on his throne splurged the 300 lbs King, staring transfixedly at the TV set.

There were about thirty people in the room, mostly girls in their teens and twenties plus half-a-dozen of the staff and aides that I had seen around the place earlier in the day. No-one was talking. Everyone was sitting or standing around, watching Elvis watching TV. Every now and then the King delivered a judgement on the show: 'that guy's stronger than Tarzan's armpits', he said at one point; 'if my aunt had nuts, she'd be my uncle', on another. Despite the distinctly Delphic lucidity of such pronouncements, they provoked an adoring *frisson* of laughter from the entourage. But to my mind, watching paint dry was more fun than partying with Elvis.

I noticed that one of the girls kept glancing over in my direction. At first I dismissed the observation as mere wishful thinking. Then I assumed she was looking for a companion she was expecting to appear through the door just behind me. But more and more I became convinced that it really was me

she was looking at. Furthermore, there was something hauntingly familiar about her. A model perhaps? An actress? A
waitress?

My thoughts were interrupted by the noisy arrival of two
men carrying guitar cases. Elvis looked round, raised a hand
and snapped his fingers. Stud leapt forward, turned off the
TV and handed a guitar to the King who listlessly strummed
a few chords while waiting for the newcomers to get their
instruments into their hands.

'This here's Chet and that's Randy,' said Elvis index-
fingering them one after the other. 'Now guys, I wanna do
some of the ol' toons. You got that?'

'Right,' growled the guys in unison, and Chet twang-
twanged straight into the intro to *That's All Right Mama* with
Randy hard on his heels. Then Elvis came in on the vocals,
his voice slip-sliding along the melody just like on Anwer's
record.

All my life I'd taken a pretty dim view of pop music, but
that evening at Graceland transformed my taste. All of a sudden, I realised just what a stuffed shirt I'd been. It was like
being born again, as the Reverend McVitie used to say.

I remember vividly the moment of my conversion. It came
over me in the middle of *Mystery Train*. I couldn't help
myself. I started beating a bongo accompaniment, Pygmy-
style, on a small wooden side-table.

Abruptly, Elvis stopped singing and the others stopped
playing, but I, thoroughly carried away, continued drum-
ming. When I looked up I saw that every face in the room was
gorping at me in astonishment. Oh dear, I seemed to have
committed a solecism.

'The house rule,' drawled Elvis languidly, 'is you play only
when you'se invited to play. You don't just come here an' do
yer own thing. Lord, things would get mighty schluffy if
everyone started bangin' tables an' things. But you, you'se

real good. You'se got natural rhythm. You ain't been invited, but you can stay 'n' play. Hey Stud, fetch the man them bongos from the Music Room.'

Over the following couple of hours we jammed our way through most of Elvis's early repertoire: *Blue Moon of Kentucky*; *Milkcow Blues Boogie*; *Baby Lets Play House*; *I Forgot to Remember to Forget*; *I'll Never Let You Go (Little Darlin')*; and many more. Playing with Elvis was exhilarating beyond my dreams and I kept having to tell myself that it wasn't a dream, it was really happening.

When we eventually stopped playing, El, as he insisted I call him, beckoned me over to talk to him.

'I wanna give you a token of my appreciation for yer contribution to our fun tonite,' said Elvis as he handed me a set of car keys.

'What's this?' I asked crassly. Elvis laughed.

'They's the keys to the pink Cadillac parked out back. It's yers. A gift from your buddy, El.'

I was astonished and touched by his gesture. Of course, a pink Cadillac was far from ideal as a motor for a man on the run. But Bokassa would be over-the-moon about it and it might just persuade him to play ball about Maxwell's book. There was the minor problem of transporting it from Memphis to Bangui . . .

As I was gathering my thoughts, Elvis led his entourage off to the Pool Room to shoot ivory balls across the baize.

I wandered over to the bar and dug a cool Coors out of the fridge.

A girl, the one who'd been looking at me, appeared from the shadows.

'You never told me you played the bongos,' she said in an English accent. 'But you can practise on mine any time you like.'

I knew that voice. My God – it was Jennifer. I hadn't recognised her in pumps and a ponytail.

'What on earth are you doing here?' I spluttered, choking on my beer.

'I'm staying with Nadine and Charlene whose daddy has a super spread in Kentucky with lots of horses. They wanted to show me Graceland and we were just standing at the gate when we were invited in for the party. How about you?'

'It's a long story.'

'Good. That means it'll take you ages and ages to tell me all the details.'

***

As ever, Jennifer got her way. She took me off to a little log cabin in the Blue Ridge Mountains for a week of walks in the woods, fireside chats and bongo practice into the wee hours.

***

Incidentally, it may be of interest to Elvis fans to learn that our 'jam session' that night was taped, the den also being a fully functional recording studio. A so-called 'bootleg' album of the songs was released some years after, with the title *That's All Right (Bongo)*. I understand that it is extremely rare and highly sought-after by collectors, though I dare say Gussie and Boy won't be hoofing round the record shops after a copy.

***

Back in Bangui, Joe and a police motorcycle escort were waiting for me at the airport to whisk me straight round to the presidential palace. Bokassa was jubilant at the news that Elvis had agreed to attend his coronation and hit a veritable state of ecstasy when I told him that a pink Cadillac was on its way as a present from his idol in Memphis. By way of celebration Bokassa ordered the radio station to play dawn-to-dusk Elvis records and decreed a public holiday. My reward was a little black velvet bag containing a score of uncut diamonds, plus the promise of my elevation to the Earldom of Bimbo come the day when the republic became an empire. He also announced that he had decided upon the ghost-writer of his autobiography – me.

I protested against this honour, arguing that I already had a job working for Mr Maxwell. Bokassa said he had contacted Monsieur Maxwell, who had agreed to my secondment to him for the duration of the project. I had just won W.C. Field's third prize – a year in Bangui.

The *modus operandi* devised by Bokassa for our collaboration was as follows: I was allocated an office in Bokassa's residence, the idea being that whenever he had a spare moment between affairs of state I would be on hand to hear the next instalment of his story; then, while he was chairing the next cabinet meeting, or whatever, I would write-up my account of what he had said. A fundamental flaw was that I'd never written anything in my life except my diary, but I decided to keep mum about this detail and muddle along as best I could. There was no point in volunteering myself as a titbit for Priscilla.

We got off to a cracking start, but as the weeks went by our sessions became less and less frequent and progress slower and slower. In fact, I got so bored I started counting sheep. Assuming that I'd eaten four lamb cutlets a day, for, say, forty-eight weeks a year, holidays excluded, for eleven years, the period of my life when it was my usual habit to repair to the Clermont Club, that amounted to 14,784 cutlets. In recent years my eating habits had been more irregular, so I estimated that 16,000 was a conservative overall count. Each animal yields fourteen cutlets, meaning I'd devoured a total of 1,142 of them. I tried to imagine a flock of that size and pondered the significance of my calculations. I came to no conclusion, save that I was going mad. I picked up the 'phone and called Maxwell in London, no mean feat from Bangui, using the special code we had agreed.

'How many encyclopaedias have you sold?' were Maxwell's opening words when he came on the line.

'That's not what I want to talk about. I'm not making any headway on Bokassa's autobiography because he's too busy to spend time with me. I hang around all day. I'm bored stupid.'

'Don't moan to me about being bored. Get out there and sell some bloody books.'

'Nobody wants encyclopaedias. They're too poor and mostly illiterate. And I'm not getting anywhere with Bokassa's biography. I'm going home.'

'Listen, sunshine, you're going nowhere till I get that manuscript. You walk out on me and you're history. Got that?'

Message received.

***

My life in Bangui settled into a regular pattern. Every morning Joe came by my hotel and drove me over to Bokassa's residence. When he had a free five minutes I would be summoned into his presence and would scribble down the next fragment of his life story. Then I would return to my office and write it up on the typewriter. On a good day I could end up with a page of typing, but some days nothing at all. So the going was pitifully snail-paced. But the situation was not entirely without compensations, since in the long lacunae I was able to brush up my French with Yvette, a Parisienne translator on Bokassa's staff. Many are the happy memories of the French lessons she gave me in the office stationery cupboard, to which we retired so that our conversation classes would not be interrupted.

One day in August, as Yvette and I were wrestling with the subjunctive, a steward appeared and informed me that there was a call for me from England. It was Maxwell.

'You're in the shit, sunshine,' he said dispensing as usual with any preliminary civilities.

'Pardon.'

'He's croaked.'

'What?'

'Your chum, Elvis. He's dead.'

'How?'

'Heart attack. He was a junkie.'

'Oh dear,' I murmured. 'Poor old El. How very sad.'

'When's my book going to be finished?' demanded Maxwell, cutting short my grieving.

'At the current rate of progress sometime around the year 2000. Bokassa's spending all his time planning his coronation. He's going to be pretty cheesed-off that Elvis won't be coming. He's set his heart on it. In fact, he may even decide to pull the plug on the book, seeing as how he only agreed to do it as a *quid pro quo* for securing Elvis's services.'

'Exactly. And that will bugger me with the frogs?'

'The frogs?' I enquired. What was he on about now?

'The French government. It's the deal. I publish a book presenting a wholesome image of their African protégé putting right all the bad publicity he's had, and they see their way to grant me some licences I need to operate in France. A bit of you scratch my back, I'll scratch yours. That's the way things work over there.'

'Ah. Now I see,' I exclaimed, as a whole kaleidoscope of mysteries suddenly shifted into focus.

'When's this sodding coronation, then?' barked Maxwell.

'Three and a half months away.'

'Can't you finish the fucking book before then? Before he knows that Elvis isn't coming.'

'But he's bound to hear of his death. That sort of news reaches even here.'

'Bugger,' said Maxwell, expressing himself with character-istic economy and eloquence. 'Bugger, bugger, bugger.'

'Supposing I break the news to him . . .' I said slowly.

'That would suit you down to the ground, wouldn't it,' interjected Maxwell. 'You just want to get the hell out of there, don't you, sunshine.'

'Yes, and here's how I'm going to do it. I'll tell him about the announcement of Elvis's death, but say that I've checked it out and know that it's really a publicity stunt.'

'He'll never believe that.'

'He might, if I tell him that Elvis's come back concert will be at his coronation. He'll be tickled pink. And in the mean-time I'll accelerate progress on the book.'

'How?'

'I'll make it up. I'll use my imagination. You don't care what's in it so long as it's flattering to Bokassa, do you?'

'No.'

'I've got the basic outline of the story, so I'll just add some heroic embellishments. You know, how he saved his school-mates from a lion or rescued a pensioner who was in the path of a charging rhino. That sort of thing.'

'Well, I suppose it'll be no different to most biographies,' said Maxwell cogitatively. 'And he can hardly complain, can he?'

I wasn't so sure about the last point, but at least I now had an escape plan.

***

The less I saw of Bokassa, the more progress I made on his autobiography and a couple of months later I had virtually finished. It was a stirring farrago of invention, based on my childhood reading of *Boys' Own Adventure* books; Bokassa swimming across crocodile infested rivers; Bokassa wrestling with lions; Bokassa out-running cheetahs; Bokassa thwarting wicked witch-doctors; and lots more of the same sort of claptrap.

I'd just about completed my labours, when one day things went badly, dangerously wrong. Imagine my horror upon entering my office to find Bokassa sitting in my chair, Yvette perched on his lap translating the manuscript for him out loud. At that moment she was relating the story of how he saved a village's manioc harvest from a bush fire by organising a colony of chimpanzees to form a chain to carry buckets of water from the river, a particularly far-fetched fabrication. My blood turned cold. I started to sweat profusely.

Bokassa looked up into my eyes. How long would it be, I wondered, before he was gouging them out with his thumbs and Priscilla the monster crocodile was feasting on my flesh? But then he burst into a broad grin.

'*C'est magnifique!*' he exclaimed. 'How did you discover all this?' he demanded, Yvette translating.

'Oh I just asked a few of the people who knew you when you were younger,' I replied with nonchalant modesty.

'What excellent memories my friends have. You know, I had forgotten a lot of these episodes, but reading them here brings them back as if it was yesterday. Now, Yvette tells me you say you have finished.'

'Yes, I've brought the story up to the present.'

'You have not finished. You must include the story of my coronation.'

'The coronation hasn't happened yet. Why don't you save it for volume II?'

'Oh no. All this here is just the prologue to how I became Emperor Jean-Bedel I of the Central African Empire. I want words and pictures of my coronation in the book. You will stay and write them.'

'As you wish,' I said, knowing that it would be pointless and probably perilous to protest. But now the Elvis dimension reared its ugly head again. With the manuscript and myself safely out of the country, as planned, there would have been no danger in sending Bokassa a telegram to say that Elvis was unfortunately indisposed. But under virtual house arrest, as I knew I would be after our conversation, it was simply suicide to rile the tyrant.

As soon as Bokassa was out of the room I made a desperate move, one I would only have made in dire emergency. I made an SOS call – to Jennifer.

***

Jennifer and her secret weapon, Victor, flew into Bangui the day before the coronation. All the hotels were full of visiting dignitaries and pressmen, but I managed to billet Victor with Joe. True to form, Jennifer insisted on staying in my single bed.

The ceremony was spectacular. Bokassa was dressed in a full-length cassock, covered in tiny pearls and decorated with a pentacle motif, with a blue satin sash over a shoulder and a chain set with previous stones round his neck. He wore white gloves and a garland of gold laurel leaves in his hair, and carried a jewel-encrusted walking stick. On arrival at the Czech-built concrete sports stadium, the stand-in for Chartres Cathedral, he made a stately progress along a long red carpet while 120 musicians played popular favourites. The throne itself took the form of a massive and magnificent gilded eagle, the seat occupying its chest cavity. Soaring above the small seated figure was a huge eagles head, and on either side great golden outstretched wings reaching 20 feet off the ground at their tips.

The ceremony went on for quite a while: a colonel presented him with a sword of office; a *chef de battalion* with a belt; a captain with the imperial sceptre; and a lieutenant with a cape bordered with ermine. Then came the crowning moment, literally, when Bokassa, like Napoleon before him 173 years earlier, placed the crown on his own head. Then he crowned his bewildered-looking wife, who became Empress Catherine.

Jennifer enjoyed herself immensely. She said she hadn't seen anything quite as deliciously tacky since the *Elvis in Las Vegas* spectacular on television at Christmas.

***

Backstage at the concert hall Victor looked splendid, a faultless impersonation of Elvis the young hillbilly hell-cat of 1957. But I was horrified.

'He's hopeless,' I exclaimed to Jennifer. 'He's twenty years too young. Even a screw-loose fan like Bokassa isn't going to believe it. He doesn't look anything like the Elvis we saw in Memphis. He should look all shagged-out.'

'There weren't any shagged-out looking Elvis impersonators who were prepared to do a concert in the Central African Republic,' she replied testily. 'You should be grateful, not carping.'

'Carping? As soon as Victor steps on to the stage I become crocodile scoff,' I moaned despondently.

Then things went from bad to worse.

Standing in the front row of the audience waiting for Elvis's performance was a familiar figure. Anwer.

'Small world, isn't it,' I said amiably having barged through the crowd to his side.

Anwer looked at me with the sort of expression that comes across peoples' faces when the step in a large mess of doggy-poo.

'Leave me alone,' he moaned, nervously eyeing the two burly C.A.R. paratroopers who accompanied me.

'How's tricks?' I continued chirpily. 'What are you doing here?'

'I'm looking after Carlos, who's with one of the Arab delegations. What about you? And who the hell are you anyway?'

'I'm managing the band,' I said, hastily improvising a story.

'You're managing Elvis Presley?'

'That's right.'

'And he's really going to play tonight? He's not dead?'

'Dead? What gave you that idea?'

'It was in the newspapers. I saw the funeral on TV. There was a massive cavalcade of cars and thousands of wreaths.'

I laughed. 'Just a publicity stunt. You don't want to believe everything you read in the papers. I'll prove it to you. Why don't you come and meet him backstage? Right now, before he goes on.'

'Meet Elvis? I'd love to,' gushed Anwer putting his responsibilities entirely out of mind.

'We'll have to hurry, or it'll be too late,' I said leading the way.

We made our way through the crush of people, skirting the metal crowd control barriers to the backstage entrance. And there was Victor, ready to go on and take the audience down memory lane.

Anwer stopped and stared, looking flabbergasted.

'He's an imposter. So are you,' he cried plunging a hand into his jacket. He didn't have time to pull the gun before the paratroopers grabbed him, handcuffed his wrists and led him away. Too bad I thought, as I waved farewell. He would have gone goggle-eyed hearing about my encounter with the real Elvis.

It had been agreeable to see Anwer again, even so fleetingly. He didn't seem to have changed much; still credulous; still impetuous; still incompetent; still a twerp. It really was

time for him to make a career change, I reflected. He just did-
n't cut the mustard as a terrorist or a bodyguard. He would
be much better suited to something less martial. A waiter or
a barman, for instance, though certainly not a chef. Or perhaps a butler.

Now though, the writing was on the wall for me and Jennifer. It was only a matter of time before someone summoned
up the courage to tell Bokassa that the so-called Elvis on stage
was twenty years too young, and ten stone too light. And then
it would be feeding time for Priscilla.

With the sound of Victor's wizard rendition of *Mystery
Train* echoing in our ears, we stealthily made our way down
to the river quayside. There, ablaze with electric lights in the
deep tropical night, was the paddle steamer *Pride of the
Oubangi* about to sail down river to Brazzaville in the Congo.

As we settled in to the first class cabin I had reserved in the
name John Smith, Jennifer caught me in an arm-lock and
jack-knifed me on to the bed. She was on top of me faster
than I could say, 'Bread rolls'.

'A deckhand told me that the boat-trip down-river to Brazzaville takes fourteen days,' she whispered in my ear as she
nuzzled her tongue inside it like a Labrador. 'That's a whole
fortnight of cosy in the Congo. Now I know why you dragged
me all this way. Oh, you wonderful wicked man . . .'

6. Lucky Goes to Hollywood

Moving to Los Angeles was Jennifer's idea. It was the perfect place for lying doggo, she explained. In Los Angeles everyone is incognito. Waitresses aren't waitresses, they're models making-do between calls. The cab driver isn't a cab driver, he's really an actor who's about to be discovered. Policemen are scriptwriters in their spare time. Shop-assistants are film directors waiting for the 'phone to ring. The laundromat man is *actually* a movie producer, a bit down on his luck at the moment. Over there they've even got a term for such types, a MAW – Model/Actress/Whatever. So I became a Whatever in Wonderland.

The other plus-point for California in Jennifer's book, was that it was the other side of the world from Robert Maxwell. She was determined that I should not return to his service, my lengthy stay in Central Africa having peeved her in no small measure. She had decided that we were going to set up home together, which wasn't compatible with 'gallivanting round the globe hobnobbing with tin-pot dictators,' as she put it. I was initially uneasy. Not so much about her predilections and expectations, but because I was under contract to Maxwell and as a gentleman the undertaking weighed on my conscience. But Jennifer insisted that the Bokassa assignment had gone so far beyond any reasonable expectations that I had honourably discharged my obligation. Such was the passion of her advocacy, I had to agree.

Money was a different matter. Maxwell owed me not only for my work but a substantial backlog of unpaid expenses. I

wanted to collect what was due to me, but Jennifer argued
that money wasn't everything and that Maxwell's next job
might cost me my life. She had a point, as usual. We did some
sums and worked out that between us we had just enough
dosh to make ends meet until something turned up. So, in the
words of the song, slightly adapted, it was 'California here we
come.'

***

As the plane touched down at Los Angeles International Airport, Jennifer announced our plan of action. She would find
our accommodation while I bought a car, thus by evening we
would be a fully-functional household. I stood guard over the
luggage in the arrivals hall, while she scanned the yellow
pages at a pay-phone. First, she called a letting agency in
Venice, the neighbourhood in which she had decided we
should set up shop, and arranged to see half-a-dozen proper-
ties. Then she wrote down the addresses of some second-
hand car vendors promising bargain basement deals, and
handed the list to me.

We wandered out into the bright sunshine and the balmy
air, but there was no time to enjoy nature's bounty. Jennifer
and the bags went into a cab and disappeared in the direction
of Venice. I jumped into the next taxi instructing the driver to
take me to the establishment that topped Jennifer's list.

Her orders were to effect my mission and rendezvous at the
letting agency at 1600 hours. If Jennifer had been born a man
she would have made a first rate Field Marshal, in the Monty
or Iron Duke class, and woe betide any Huns or Froggies who
got in her way. She had God-given organisational skills and
was a natural commander of men. Thus it was decidedly disconcerting to realise that at present the extent of her command consisted of yours truly.

***

'How much money you got to spend, man?' demanded the shifty-looking, gum-chewing, youth manning the office at the used car lot off Wilshire Boulevard. He was wearing blue-jeans, a white t-shirt, an unbuttoned, untucked maroon shirt with the name 'Brad' picked out in canary-coloured thread on the breast pocket, and battered plimsolls. An unprofessional, not to mention unprepossessing, attire for a car salesman, I thought, but Jennifer had warned me to expect any sort of scruffiness in California. Mind you, nothing could have prepared me for the way he wore his cap, being positioned on his head so that the long peak covered the nape of his neck. Brad plainly didn't know the difference between front and back. Or right and left, or right and wrong, most likely. Probably the sort of misfit Gussie had in mind when he advocated mercy culling.

'About $2,000,' I told him.

'You lookin' for a bicycle, maybe?' replied the lippy whipper-snapper.

'Not a bicycle, an automobile,' I said slowly, using the vernacular term just in case he hadn't grasped why I was standing in a used car lot. Maybe the hat was restricting the blood supply to his brain?

'No shit!,' exclaimed Brad, pawing the ground with a plimsoll as he spoke. 'Trouble is, mister, that kinda bread don't buy a lotta automobile round here. But we got some wrecks out back. Come an' take a look.'

'You from Boston?,' he asked as we made our way to the rear of the lot.

'No, I'm English,' I replied. We halted in front of a rank of rusty vehicles of seriously unroadworthy appearance.

'A Brit, huh, well I'll be darned. I got just the machine for you. Word is, this one here was used in one of them James Bond movies.'

He pointed to the most dilapidated of the collection, an

Aston Martin that was a sorry shadow of its former self.

'Strange to think that I might have driven it in its prime,' I remarked wistfully.

'Come again?' said Brad.

'Oh, it's just that I almost screen-tested for the part of James Bond.'

'Holy shit!' exclaimed Brad. 'You in the movies? I had you figured for one of them up-tight East coast types. Hey look, man, I've been workin' on this screen-play. I'd be mighty grateful if you'd take a look.'

His voice and attitude had radically changed gear. Gone was the surly street-wise sneer. My remark about the screen-test had him all fired-up, a bright-eyed bushy-tailed Brad.

'How grateful, Brad?'

'Say, I reckon I might be able to help you out. I got somethin' to show you.'

We made our way back through the rows of cars, Brad rabbiting all the time about his screen-play which seemed to be about motor-bike gangs.

'There she is,' said Brad, flashing a finger at a car of an unfamiliar design.

'What is it?'

'A Nissan Cedric. Kind of collector's number these days. But trusty as genuine Ousley.'

'It says $4,000' I said, reading the sign on the windscreen.

'Yours for $2,000. Cash.'

'Pity about the colour,' I ventured, referring to the lurid metallic peppermint green paint work.

'It's a cryin' shame. Would be worth twice the money if some dumb-arse hadn't re-sprayed her that way. That's how come I can sell her to you at a crazy price. Just as long as you can see a way to check-out my screen-play, of course.'

Given our delicate financial situation I wasn't going to look a gift horse in the mouth, even one the colour of mouthwash.

'Brad, I would be delighted to look at your screen-play,' I said expansively. 'It's a deal.'

We went into the office and did the paperwork, Brad fishing out his manuscript while I scrutinised the registration documents and the warranty.

'There it is,' said Brad, handing over a copy of his opus. 'Well, I guess I'll be hearing from you?'

'Don't hold your breath, Brad,' I murmured as I picked up the script and the car-keys.

Driving out of the car lot, I felt I'd just won a hand of poker with a pair of twos. Not that I had any intention of not honouring my undertaking to Brad. I glanced across at the passenger seat and looked at his screenplay. Every time I went out in the car I'd look at his screenplay. But I certainly wouldn't pick it up and read it.

★★★

In the meantime, Jennifer had settled on a charming apartment on the first floor of a white clap-boarded house a couple of streets back from the beach in Venice. It was a modest abode appropriate to our means, comprising bedrooms, sitting room, bathroom and kitchen. With the sun streaming in through the slatted blinds it looked very *House and Garden*, very Jennifer. All the walls were white and the floors were varnished boards strewn with muted dhurries. The cane furniture featured cream-coloured coverings, save for the big bed which had a powder blue counterpane with a scallop shell motif. Contrary to my intimations on the plane over, she had plumped for a one-bed home. Oh dear, it looked like shut-eye would become an endangered species.

Venice, our neighbourhood, was something of a surprise. The name had conjured a vision of refinement and tasteful tranquillity, but the reality was the opposite. The streets, especially the sea-side boardwalk, were thronged by people in t-shirt, shorts and sunglasses, most of them on roller-skates. Even the buskers and beggars wore skates, wheeling along as they strummed guitars or gave tiresome displays of fire-eating or juggling while they passed the hat. Even more manky than Carnaby Street was my opinion, but Jennifer relished the spectacle. She was especially keen on walks that encompassed Muscle Beach, a nearby stretch of sand that was the haunt of the body-building fraternity. Now, I'm not a great fan of spectator sports, though I enjoy watching a good game of football or rugger on TV. What I've never understood is the appeal of watching men with over-developed pectorals lifting dumb-bells, but Jennifer was happy to stand there for hours gazing at the gorillas pumping-iron or doing press-ups. Oh well, as the French waiter said to the actress, *chacun a son goût.*

Repelled by the trendy rabble on our doorstep, I spent my time indoors, reading, watching TV, or playing cards with Jennifer. Sometimes we just chatted, telling stories or musing about life and the way of the world. She took a close interest in my tales of my encounters years ago with the Italian film director Vittorio de Sica and the Hollywood producer Cubby Broccoli, who had both suggested that I went into the movies. Cubby, as I have mentioned, wanted me to screen-test for the lead role in the James Bond films. 'You've got it all,' he told me, 'the looks, the breeding, the pride.' But I was too bashful, and then along came Sean Connery.

'Do your regret your decision?' she enquired tenderly.

'Maybe I do, now,' I said, pondering how different life would have been if I had become a film star. I might even have got to work with David Niven, without a troupe of chimpanzees.

Jennifer and I got on pretty well living at close quarters. She was affectionate, amusing and easy-going, that is so long as I stuck to the rules she laid down. Gambling was out.

Smoking was forbidden inside the apartment because of the pong, while boozing was banned outside the home, just in case I got stinko and dropped my guard like Lourenço Marques. I was required to put out the rubbish, load the dishwasher and do the shopping. Initially I was also charged with the cooking, but Jennifer soon thought better of that. The boudoir business was a daily duty, with gala bastinado sessions on Sundays. All in all, my lifestyle was radically reformed. Yet these 'improvements,' as Jennifer called them, were but forerunners for her big idea. She had decided that I was going to be in the movies nonetheless, and applied her formidable talents to this end.

***

'What's your stage name?' asked Lisa, an agent whose name Jennifer had found in *Academy Players*. The words blurred into each other in her laid-back, California-casual drawl, and because she was lolly-popping the end of a ball-point pen.

'John Smith,' I replied, being keen to revert to that everyman appellation and to shed the Toots du Maurier tag with which I had always been uncomfortable.

Lisa pulled a sour face, reminding me of Squiffy Marchmain chewing the slice of lemon at the bottom of his gin and tonic.

'It stinks,' she said bluntly.

'Why?'

'Too many negative connotations. Makes me think of that dweeb who sexually harassed Pocahontas. And too bland. Who's gonna remember a name like that? You need somethin' with pizzazz. A name that sticks in the head like a brain tumour.'

'How about, Toots du Maurier?' I ventured resignedly.

'Oh, that's good,' said Lisa nodding enthusiastically, the shoulder pads in her turquoise raw-silk jacket rustling gently as she moved her head. 'That's got class. *Cachet*, even. We'll go with it.'

My stage name settled to her satisfaction, Lisa's attitude to my career became distinctly more positive. She quizzed me about my acting experience and was plainly impressed by the accounts of my encounters with David Niven, Cubby Broccoli and Vittorio di Sica, all considerably embroidered with Jennifer's suggestions. The rest of what I told her about my training at RADA and repertory theatre experience was a cock and bull yarn invented by Jennifer, but Lisa swallowed it hook, line and sinker. Plainly I was telling her what she wanted to hear. The interview rounded off with some practical questions.

'Nationality?'

'Jamaican.'

'Got a green car?'

'Yes,' I replied defensively, expecting some snide remarks of the sort Jennifer made every time we went out for a drive. But she scribbled something in her book and continued with the questions.

'Sag?'

'Yes, I suppose so,' I replied in a defensive tone of voice, rather taken aback at what I took to be a forthright reference to my tummy, which I had to admit seemed to have rounded out somewhat since I had been enjoying Jennifer's home cooking. Oh well, I would just have to cut out the cutlets for a while.

Lisa completed the paperwork, parking her signature with a flutter of the wrist at the foot of the page. I signed on the other side.

'Excellent,' she said, sitting back in the big black leather executive chair. She smiled for the first time, tiny hairlines fanning across her taught tanned cheeks. 'You know, Toots, you're kinda different from most of the actors I represent.

There's somethin' special about you. An unusual naive quality. Feral even. I think, maybe, I can see the makings of another John Travolta.'

Not having heard of John Travolta I was unable to comment, but I had my own role model in mind.

'Why not David Niven?'

Lisa pulled another face. 'Travolta is box office; Niven is Stone Age,' she declared dismissively. She pushed a button on the intercom on her desk. 'Any messages, Sharon?'

'There was a call from the Allan Carr movie that's shooting on the MGM lot,' said her secretary over the squawk-box. 'One of the guys has gone sick and they want a replacement for tomorrow.'

'Call them back and tell them the replacement's name is Toots du Maurier.'

She looked over at me. 'Well, it seems like it's your lucky day. Your Hollywood career has just started.'

'Thank you,' I muttered in a small strangled voice. I was in shock. Up to that moment, I had regarded the whole think as a joke. Frankly, I had only gone along to humour Jennifer. I had never expected to get a job, and yet here I was joining the cast of a Hollywood movie like a star-is-born story come true. But reality was starting to elbow its way into my thoughts. What had Jennifer got me into now?

'I can see that you're overcome,' Lisa said gently. 'That's cute. Don't feel embarrassed. Sharon will give you the shooting schedule on the way out. Go for it, Toots.'

It was only later, during Jennifer's blow-by-blow debriefing of my session with Lisa, that certain misunderstandings came to light. Lisa hadn't been referring to the colour of the Nissan Cedric or to my *en-bon-point*; she wanted to know if I had a green-card work permit, and whether I had membership of the Screen Actors Guild, or SAG for short. Of course, I had neither, although I had inadvertently told her I had both. But there was no need for panic. An acquaintance of Jennifer's, an Argentinean called Enrico, a Mr Universe who worked out on Muscle Beach, proved to be a professional forger and was able to supply me with the requisite documents that very evening for just $500.

***

The motion-picture in which I made my screen debut was a far cry from the delightful derring-do films David Niven was wont to appear in. It was a lamentable pop music extravaganza called *Can't Stop The Music*. The plot was unfathomable, but had something to do with the antics of a moustachioed barber's shop sextet, comprising a red indian, a policeman, a construction worker, a GI, a cowboy and a rocker, who ponced around in sequinned *lamé* costumes. The ensemble went under the name Village People. Village Idiots was nearer the mark.

I have never been a big fan of musicals, but I had a distinct recollection that they contained bevies of gorgeous girls kicking their legs in the air and I confess to loosening my collar as I piloted the Nissan Cedric over to the MGM lot that morning. But in fact, girls were as plentiful as snowflakes in the Sahara. The reason, it transpired, was that they were shooting a sequence set in the gymnasium of the Young Mens' Christian Association. I joined the troupe of gymnasts clad in shorts, singlet and running shoes who performed callisthenics in the background while the Village People chasseyed through an upbeat ditty entitled *YMCA*. I soon got into the swing of it. In fact, the routines reminded me of a Burns Night ceilidh, and I thoroughly enjoyed myself. Later they filmed us diving into a swimming pool one after another clad only in skimpy costumes. That must have been how I got the bout of flu that put me to bed for a week and brought my budding career as a Hollywood actor to an end.

Romanian village after Anwer and I had lunch.

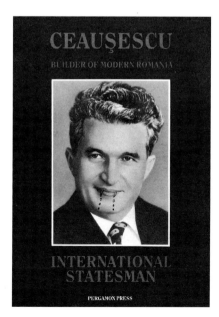

Nicolae Ceausescu, who
honoured me with the
Order of Vlad. Artwork by
Anwer.

Off to rehearsals with the Village People.

Evacuated from Port Stanley. Jennifer's disguise (black scarf, 2nd row) fooled even our fellow Argentine POWs.

Elvis as I never knew him.

The Earl of Bimbo (yours truly, *right*), *en route* to hide amongst the Pygmies.

Emperor Bokassa, who chose me as his biographer. His coronation was a momentous occasion for all concerned.

Penal servitude. Modelling headgear in Castro's tobacco fields.

Out shopping. No-one appeared to recognise me.

Snapped by Jennifer at Cap Ferrat, I was unrecognisable in my new hairstyle.

Anwer, my minder, kept a close eye on me.

My car.

The *Lady Ghislaine* – where I presented my expenses
bill to Robert Maxwell.

Anwer undercover as Maxwell's bodyguard. He has made a much better butler.

Give me the girl, give me the moonlight, give me a vodka martini – and leave the rest to me.

Lying between the sheets convalescing provided me with an opportunity for reflection. What the blazes was I doing becoming an actor? That was no way to lie doggo. Like as not, Detective Inspector Roy Ransom, the Scotland Yard sleuth who was leading the hunt for me according to the newspapers, would turn out to be a big fan of the Village People. As soon as he wandered into the local Odeon for an eyeful and earful of *Can't Stop The Music*, my cover would be blown. A career as a screen actor was absurd for someone in my position. I decided that I wouldn't be going back to see Lisa.

Jennifer accepted my decision more readily than I'd expected.

'Oh well,' she responded, 'in that case you'll have to make your career behind the camera.'

'What do you mean?'

'You'll have to become a film director.'

★★★

Although the piggy-bank was almost empty, I decided that we should dress up smartly and go out on the town to celebrate Jennifer's birthday. After all, you're only young once.

Over dinner in fashionable Ma Maison, I told her about an embarrassing encounter on the set of *Can't Stop The Music*. Wandering around between takes watching the proceedings, I found myself face to face with the producer and an assistant. Feeling rather like a voyeur caught in the act, I smiled guiltily and said 'Hi'. They nodded. The silence was unbearable, so I made some sociable chit-chat about the weather, as one does.

'Nice and sunny today,' I bantered. 'Mind you, I suppose it won't last. Do you think we'll have rain tomorrow?'

They eyed me warily and backed away.

'Don't worry he's just a dancer. He's harmless,' the assistant reassured his companion as they turned on their heels and made off at a brisk trot. I asked Jennifer what she made of their behaviour.

'Very reasonable,' she replied, much to my surprise. 'They must have thought you were talking like an escapee from a funny farm. No body mentions the weather in southern California. There's nothing to say. It's non-stop sunshine. Who was the producer? Who were you talking about?'

'I can't remember his name. Why does it matter?'

'Of course it matters,' she replied irritably. 'He could be a useful contact. Think about it. Concentrate.'

I closed my eyes and focused my mind on the name until my temples throbbed. Suddenly it came to me. 'Allan Carr,' I boomed, a sense of psychological and even physical catharsis surging through me.

'Hey, you know Allan Carr?' loudly interjected a man sitting at the adjacent table. He was short, bald and rotund and attired in an array of expensive separates that should never have formed an ensemble: white patent loafers; magenta and emerald plaid slacks; an eau de Nile blazer; a cerise silk shirt worn half unbuttoned to show off a gold ingot suspended from the chain round his neck.

'That's right,' I said stiffly, annoyed at having our conversation interrupted by a stranger.

'Jeez, I got a heap of respect for Allan. I mean, what a track record. *Saturday Night Fever, Grease,* and now the new picture. That guy must be makin' a packet.'

'Is he a friend of yours?' I enquired.

'Sure. Oh, don't get me wrong. We're not personally acquainted. I mean I've never met the guy face to face. We're both busy people. But I can relate to where he's at. I guess you know him real good?'

'You could say, we've been working together.' I replied evasively. Plainly this stranger hadn't eavesdropped our whole conversation.

He laughed uneasily.

'Jeez, it must be great being in the movie business. Workin' with the stars and movers and shakers like Allan Carr. Boy, I envy you guys, I really do. So what are you Brits doin' in town? No, no, don't tell me, let me guess. I reckon you're some big shot exec producer or co-finance guy or somethin' like that. I mean look at the way you dress. You don't look like no schmuck to me.'

'Not quite,' said Jennifer, before I had time to open my mouth to disabuse him of these delusions. 'He's a director and I'm a scriptwriter. We work together as a team. I'm Jennifer Moneypenny and this is Toots du Maurier.'

'Great to meet you,' said the stranger leaning across the gangway and shaking our hands. 'Marty Pretzel is the name,' He opened his wallet, extracted a couple of cards and handed them over. I read:

Marty J. Pretzel Jr.
President, Gourmet Pet Treats Inc.
"Creature comforts for contented critters"

'What is a "pet treat"?' I asked bewilderedly. Marty J. Pretzel Jr. looked taken-aback.

'Cocoa butter candy *dragés* for quadruped companions,' he replied pat. I grappled with the reply for what felt like an age, and then I got it.

'You mean chocolate drops for dogs.'

'Not just any old chocolate,' protested Marty, 'gourmet cocoa butter product from Belgium. And the finest fillings, fondant, regular and crunchy.'

'Fascinating, I'm sure,' I said flatly. 'It has been very nice meeting you Mr Pretzel, but now we must get back to our meal.'

But Marty wasn't to be put off so easily.

'I heard there was some Brit movie people in town. David Putnam and some other guys. You workin' with them?'

'We're good friends, but we're independents,' said Jennifer. I bit my bottom lip, trying to stop myself gaping openly at her outrageous lies.

'Well, what are you guys up to? What's your trip?'

'We've got a couple of projects in concept that we're looking to put into development,' she said. I had no idea what she was talking about.

'Sounds interesting,' said Marty. He looked at his watch. 'Say, have you got a card? Let's stay in touch. It would be great to see you guys again.'

'I'll write down the number,' volunteered Jennifer, scrawling it on the inside cover of a book-match. What possessed her to do so was beyond me, but I kept mum.

'Much obliged,' said Marty putting it in his pocket. 'I gotta be gettin' along now. Got a meeting about the launch of our latest product. Chewing-gum for cats. Anchovy flavour, Tuna flavour, Herring flavour, they just go crazy for it. I'll tell you all about it sometime. See you soon.' And he was gone.

'What a droll little man,' remarked Jennifer gaily.

'He's after something,' I replied.

'Of course, he is,' she said. 'And so are we.'

★★★

We didn't have to wait long for a call from Marty J. Pretzel Jr. Two days later he rang and suggested that we should come to his place in Beverley Hills that evening for drinks. He said that he had an idea to run by us. I had reservations, but she-who-must-be-obeyed was adamant. So we went.

Jennifer said that it was important that I looked the part of an English film director and dragged me off on a tour of the local thrift shops to buy the appropriate kit. At the end of our expedition, I was dressed in jhodpurs, knee-length chestnut riding boots, a baggy white shirt, yellow silk cravat and a three-button black blazer. I looked like a throwback to the 1920s, but that didn't worry me. In fact, I realised how ill-at-ease I'd been attired in all those so-called comfortable casuals and felt much more at home in these proper togs.

Marty's place was a big, white, sprawling ranch house perched near the summit of a hill. The approach was up a steep winding drive, lushly decked with bougainvillea and oleander.

The front door opened on to a massive reception space the size of two tennis courts. Decoratively, the style was Tower of London. It was like a museum of militaria; guns, antique and modern, bayonets, swords, even suits of armour, lined the walls, all neatly labelled. Marty was plainly a serious weapons collector.

The far side of the room was one large picture window looking out onto the patio and the pool, and beyond in the distance the sparkling lights of Century City. Built in the 1940s for a long-forgotten B-features star, Marty's place had been home to a line of Hollywood actors, producers and directors whose names were recited reverentially as, got up in another unspeakably gaudy outfit, he escorted us to the poolside.

Lying on a comfortable lounger by the floodlit water, sipping a vodka martini, the warm Santa Ana breeze stroking my skin and gently rustling the dangling datura trumpets, it was natural to imagine that Marty J. Pretzel Jr. had just about everything one could want. Wrong. Marty was a deeply dissatisfied man, and in a hell of a hurry to purchase the happiness he craved.

Something stirred in the depths of the pool. A bouquet of bubbles broke the surface, and then a long dark shadow appeared. I was horror-struck, for a moment convinced that Priscilla, Bokassa's man-eating crocodile, had followed me to

Marty's pool. But the creature turned out to be a young woman in a diving mask with an aqualung on her back.

'Hey Mitzy, come over and say hi,' called Marty as she clambered out of the water up the pool ladder.

'Mitzy's an actress,' volunteered Marty, sounding just a little too eager to explain things. 'She's screen-testing for the part of a mermaid who falls in love with a scuba diver. It's mostly shot under water, so she's practising in my pool. It's a big deal for her, so I wanna help out.'

Mitzy removed the face mask and breathing tube and shed the oxygen-cylinder at the poolside. She waved to us.

'Hi everybody,' she trilled and blew a kiss off her palm in our direction just like a fully paid-up luvvie.

'Ain't she cute?' said Marty, as Mitzy wiggled carefully towards us, her gait emphasising her curvaceous figure especially the *Playboy* centre-fold proportioned breasts, just about stowed in the skimpiest of bikinis.

'Mitzy, I want you to meet my friends Toots and Jennifer. They're from England. You know where England is?'

'Oh sure,' said Mitzy. 'Near Boston, right?'

'Yeah, close,' said Marty sheepishly. 'Now run along and have shower and I'll join you when I've finished with my guests.'

'See you later,' breezed Mitzy as she took her leave. I concluded that it wasn't Mitzy's mind that was the key to her friendship with Marty.

'I'm gonna level with you guys,' said Marty, leaning forward towards us in the deck-chair, waving his Chivas-on-the-rocks so that the gyrating ice cubes chimed against the glass.

'I gotta a business that turns over $300 million. I got a house worth $4 million. I got a Porsche, a Rolls Royce and a couple of run-abouts. I got a Matisse in the lounge and a Picasso in the John. Just a small one. I even got an Angus Calder out here at the poolside.' He nodded towards some sheets of metal that might have been refugees from a scrap yard.

'But there's something I ain't got. Know what that is?'

'Love?' I ventured gingerly.

Marty laughed.

'Jeez, nah. I've been there. I've run through three wives and three divorces. Cost me plenty. What I'm talking about is *respect*. There's only one way to get respect in this town – the movies. If you ain't in the movies, you ain't nobody. So I figure, it's time to get into pictures. Become a player. But that's easier said than done, 'cos everyone knows everyone in the movie business, and if they don't know you they don't wanna know you, 'cos if you was worth knowin' someone else would know you. See what I mean? I mean, everyone's tied up. But then I meet you guys and I says to myself, maybe as a new act in town you ain't so plugged in. Maybe we can do business together?'

'We're pretty tied up,' I said, hoping to staunch these fantasies before matters got out of hand, 'and plugged in too.'

'Not that tied up,' contradicted Jennifer. 'What do you have in mind?'

'A partnership. Me as producer, you guys as director and scriptwriter.'

'We agree,' said Jennifer. I was flabbergasted and unable to suppress a gasp of astonishment. My next gasp was of pain, as Jennifer's heel dug into my shin. Fortunately Marty was far too pre-occupied with deal-making to notice my writhings.

'Humungeous,' pronounced Marty triumphally. 'Now this calls for a celebration.'

He pressed a bell-button and a Filipino maid appeared carrying a bottle of Dom Perignon and three glasses on a tray.

Marty opened the fizz and poured the drinks. We toasted our partnership.

'So, how about running some ideas past me,' he said as we

lowered our glasses. Marty wasn't one for wasting time on idle pleasantries.

'Not now,' said Jennifer firmly, but in a friendly way. 'I'm working on something at the moment that I think you might like, but I'd prefer to show it to you when it's fully-worked.'

'When will that be?' said Marty, sounding a little disappointed.

'It depends.'

'On what?'

'Money,' Jennifer said brazenly.

'How much?'

'$5,000 for a treatment. $10,000 for a first draft screenplay, plus points, of course,' she replied to my astonishment. How did she know all this about treatments and points, whatever they might be.

'What's it about?'

'It's a Vietnam picture.'

'Oh yeah? *The Dearhunter* has done tremendous box office. Is it something like that?'

'Sort of like that.'

'Oh great,' enthused Marty, getting out his chequebook. 'Skip the treatment. Let's go straight to the screenplay. I don't wanna waste no more time.'

★★★

'What have you done?' I wailed as soon as the Nissan Cedric nosed out of Marty's drive. 'You've taken his money for a non-existent screenplay. You're no scriptwriter. And I can't direct films for toffee. This is madness.'

'Be quiet,' said Jennifer measuredly. 'I know what I'm doing. Lucky, I have something to say that may upset you.'

What had she got in mind now? A bank hold-up, maybe?

'When you were in Africa for all that time,' she continued, 'do you know what I was doing?'

'I give up.'

'I was living in London with a film-maker. Actually, you've met him. He's called Klaus. He directed the commercial that David Niven made with the chimpanzees at Cap Ferrat.'

I remembered him. An absolute stinker.

'Well, I've seen the film business inside out. I know what goes on. The scripts, the rewrites, the filming, the cameras, the editing, the lot. It's easy-peasy, I tell you. The only difficult part is getting your hands on some money, but that problem is being taken care of by our fairy godfather, Marty Pretzel.'

'Look, old sausage, I can't direct a film and I doubt if you can write a screenplay.'

'Don't worry so much. Tomorrow you're going to enrol at film school to learn the basics. Marty's money will pay the fees. When it comes to the actual shooting, we'll hire a top-notch cameraman who'll tell you what to film. That's what happens anyway.'

'But where are we going to get a script from? And why about Vietnam?'

'Vietnam films are popular at the moment. Don't worry about the script. Where there's a will there's a way,' she remarked enigmatically. 'Just remember, there's no such thing as an original idea especially in Tinseltown.'

We drove on in silence. I grappled with the last couple of sentences, but failed to make much sense of them. We were almost in Santa Monica when Jennifer spoke again.

'Aren't you jealous?'

'Not at all. I feel rather sorry for him, actually.'

'Why?' she demanded.

'All that work and money, and he's so miserable.'

'Not Marty, you fool. About Klaus.'

'Oh him. Well you're not with him any more, you're here with me. So what does it matter?'

'So you wouldn't mind if I had an affair with Marty?'

'With Marty? You find Marty attractive?'

'No, I don't, but that's not the point.'

'Well, if you don't fancy him, why do you want to have an affair with him?'

'I'm not going to have an affair with him. But would you be jealous if I did?'

It was on the tip of my tongue to point out that since she had just declared that she wasn't going to have an affair with Marty there was nothing for me to be jealous about, but I decided to keep my peace. One thing I've learned the hard way is never to argue with a woman who's hell-bent on a quarrel. Not unless wresting with a bear or playing patsy with a panther is your idea of fun.

***

Matters worked out just as Jennifer had envisaged. I was promptly packed off to film school while she busied herself with the script. I stood out a bit from the rest of the students on account of my age and accent, the jhodpurs and riding boots too, the others wearing jeans and trainers, but I soon settled down and became thoroughly absorbed in my studies.

Jennifer was rather secretive about what she was up to. She told me about her visits to the Los Angeles Central Library, but wouldn't reveal exactly what she was researching or allow me to read her scribblings. I have to admit that after a couple of weeks I was beginning to wonder whether she had bitten off more than she could chew, but I was mistaken.

Returning home from school one evening, I was greeted by a joyful Jennifer. She sat me down on the sofa, put a glass of wine in one hand and a neatly typed manuscript in the other. *Downriver*, a screenplay by Jennifer Moneypenny and Toots du Maurier, read the title page.

'My name shouldn't be here,' I said. 'This is all your work. You deserve full credit.'

'Nonsense. The purpose of the exercise is to promote your Hollywood career, remember.'

So it was, I recalled. But everything that had happened to me in the last fortnight had been so strange and so hectic that I'd lost touch with the basics or common-sense. In fact, reading a screenplay written by me that I'd never seen before, was pretty much par for the course.

In a nutshell, the story of *Downriver* concerned the tribulations of a debonair French rubber planter and a prim American Peace Corps worker who escaped the murderous Vietcong by sailing a clapped-out motor launch through the Mekong Delta. A Jesuit missionary came in at some point and a few other characters, but basically the story concerned the development of the relationship between the two principals as they were confronted by rapids, ambushes, crocodiles, mosquitoes and even a firing squad when they were captured. But they survived and lived happily ever after. It was exciting, touching and witty. I'd never read a screenplay before, but it seemed like a winner to me.

***

Marty took the same view. He reckoned a budget of $15 million would be about right and immediately set about raising the finance to make his breakthrough as a movie producer.

A week-or-so later we received a summons to attend a conference up at the house in Beverley Hills. Marty was in sparkling form, and dressed like a neon bill-board to match his mood.

'There's been a lot of interest from a lot of people,' Marty purred proudly. 'It's still early days, but from the reactions so far I think we've got to make a few changes. Just minor cosmetic things.'

'Such as?' said Jennifer. There was a hint of irritation in her voice.

'That bit when they get captured by the Germans? A number of people have asked about that. They say there weren't no Germans in Vietnam.'

Jennifer paused. Marty had a point. But she had the answer.

'It's a maverick unit of fanatical Nazis who were hand chosen by Hitler and sent to fight with the Japanese in the Second World War. They've been hiding out in the jungle ever since, refusing to surrender. For them the war never ended.'

'Wow,' said Marty. 'That's a new angle. I never heard anyone use that one before. That's good. We could even get a swastika on the publicity. That always helps box office. Say, suppose we get Toshiro Mifune to play a Jap? Would do wonders for the takings in Tokyo. Write some Japs in there too, will you.'

'Wouldn't they be rather elderly by now?' I observed. I felt a sharp pain in my shin under the table and recognised Jennifer's footwork.

'What else?' she asked Marty.

'Well, there's the Jesuit missionary. Some of the parties who may be interested in backin' the picture ain't so keen on the priest. They want, well, more balance in the casting.'

'Balance?' enquired Jennifer.

'Yeah. Broaden the box office appeal. So we make him a rabbi.'

'What's he doing up-country in Vietnam?' I asked. 'Not a lot of synagogues in those parts.' My reward for this contribution was another kick. I decided henceforth to keep my thoughts to myself.

'Listen, smart-arse,' said Marty plainly annoyed by my interventions, 'you work out what the fuck he's doin' up there. That's your job, not mine.'

'Fine,' said Jennifer mildly. 'We'll do that.'

'And the lead guy,' said Marty continuing his catalogue of changes. 'He's Italian not French, got it?'

'Italian,' exclaimed Jennifer.

'Listen,' said Marty irritably. 'Some of the people I know have good connections in Palermo. There's a chance we can get co-production money out of them if the guy's a wop.'

'But Vietnam was a French colony. There were no Italian connections,' said Jennifer. Marty frowned. He was becoming touchier and touchier about even the slightest hint of criticism.

'Maybe he's sellin' pizza, or something. Use your fuckin' imagination.'

'Who do you have in mind for the part?' said Jennifer, moving on matter-of-factly.

'Travolta's hot. He's the front runner.'

'But he does song and dance pictures like *Saturday Night Fever* and *Grease.*'

'Yeah, well some people think that Vietnam has peaked and musicals are where the money is now. Me, I'm not so sure, but why not play safe and put in some routines. That bit where he gets covered in leeches would be great set to song.'

'I was wondering about Meryl Streep for the female lead,' volunteered Jennifer. 'She's got the poise and the authority, but also the vulnerability. I see her character as. . .'

'Interesting idea. But I was thinking of trying out an unknown. Launch a new face and a new career. And save a heap of money.'

'Do you have anyone in mind?'

'Err, yeah, actually, I do,' replied Marty with uncharacteristic diffidence.

'Who?'

'An actress name of Miss Mitzy Mazoomas. Friend of

mine, as it happens,' he said looking a little flushed. 'You met her, poolside.'

'Maybe we should set the picture underwater,' said Jennifer a little sourly. 'Anything else?'

'Just the title. The reaction to *Downriver* has been kinda downbeat. So I've re-titled. The picture's now called *Loveboat to Saigon!*'

***

Imagine my surprise to see a tank lumbering along the road towards me as I approached our apartment in the Nissan Cedric one afternoon after film school a couple of weeks later. But strangeness is the way of life in Los Angeles, so I was unconcerned. That is until it swung off the road and ploughed right up to our front door, making a dreadful mess of the grass and trampling Jennifer's lovingly planted flower beds. I braked and pulled up alongside the curb a little distance away. At that moment the side door of the house opened and Jennifer emerged carrying her overnight bag. She waved to me and ran towards the car, a clump of jacaranda masking her movements from the tank. As she plunged into the passenger seat there was a loud explosion and the roof of the house blew skywards, just like in the movies. Then thousands of wooden splinters showered down, tap-tapping on the roof and bonnet like a round of applause.

'Fancy some tea at the Bel-Air Hotel?' Jennifer inquired as she got in. 'I'm just dying for a cuppa.'

'Sounds less dangerous than hanging around here,' I replied, executing a stunt-man style getaway, taking out a row of stick-mounted mailboxes and the plastic heron that graced a neighbour's lawn.

'What's going on?' I asked as we sped off towards Westwood.

'It's Marty. He's gone mad.'

'That was Marty in the tank?'

'Yes.'

'Where did he get a tank?'

'Army surplus, I suppose. You can buy anything in this country.'

'But why?'

'He likes playing with guns. You must have noticed all those weapons in his drawing room.'

'Why did he come round to our house in a tank and blow it to bits?'

'As I said, he's gone bonkers. He 'phoned up an hour ago and said that we'd humiliated him and that he was coming round to get even. I threw some things in a bag and waited for you to show up. Thank God you appeared when you did.'

'But *why* has Marty gone mad?' I asked. There was something about Jennifer's explanation that wasn't quite 20 shillings to the pound.

'Apparently there was an article about him in a trade paper this morning. Rather rude, so it seems. You know how sensitive he is to criticism, but he's definitely over-reacting.'

'Why take it out on us?'

'From what I could make out from his ranting and raving, the paper was ridiculing his ambition to get into the movies. He seems to hold us responsible.'

'I think we ought to have a look at this article,' I said easing the Nissan Cedric on to a slip road leading from the freeway to a large shopping mall. While Jennifer made a quick dash for the paperstand, I stayed at the wheel gunning the engine in case we had to make a dash for it. We were behaving as if we were Bonnie and Clyde. Life felt like a movie.

Jennifer read, while I drove. The story was readily found – it was the front page. Under the headline 'Dog Food King Flogs A Dog', it stated that pet-food manufacturer Marty J. Pretzel Jr. was trying to raise money to make a movie about

the Vietnam war. In fact, the property was a thinly disguised
update of the John Huston classic, *The African Queen,* and
extensive chunks of the original screenplay had been lifted
verbatim. When the owners of the original had seen the script
they had instigated legal proceedings. Mr Marty J. Pretzel Jr.
was the laughing stock of Hollywood.

Now I understood how Jennifer had produced such a stun-
ning screenplay. She had copied it out in the library.

'Is that how the Germans got into it?' I asked.

'Yes,' she replied sheepishly. 'They're in *The African
Queen.* I must have forgotten to make the change. It's right at
the end and I was in such a rush. At first I tried to put it in my
own words, but the original sounded better. And it had to be
done so quickly. Anyway, I thought whatever I did would be
so mangled in the rewrites that it would be unrecognisable.
That's what usually happens.'

'Poor old Marty,' I said sentimentally. 'I suppose he'll get
locked up for what he's done.'

'Good job too. He deserves to be behind bars for what he
was proposing to do to our work.'

'I say, old sausage, both our names are on that script. It's
possible that someone is after us for that. I think we'd better
make tracks. I'd prefer not to be arrested for stealing a screenplay.'

'Me too,' said Jennifer. 'You know, the other day I was
reading why the film industry had originally located in southern California.'

'Something to do with the sunshine, wasn't it?'

'Yes. But the other reason was that it's only a couple of
hours drive from Mexico. Just in case things got, well, out of
hand.'

'Or out of luck,' I replied, pointing the Nissan Cedric
south towards Tijuana.

7. Cutlets Galore

The Falkland Islands may look no bigger than a couple of swatted gnats on most maps, but they have, in fact, a slightly larger land surface than Belgium. The Falklands and Belgium also have similarly sized populations of some 10 million, though respectively of penguins and people. The human inhabitants of the Falklands – who call themselves *kelpers* – number about 1,800. Their main livelihood is sheep-farming, there being 650,000 of the beasts at the last count. Sheep are the mainstay not only of the islands' economy but of the everyday diet – so much so that mutton is known vernacularly as *365*. For a lover of lamb cutlets, a sort of earthly paradise.

Actually, I didn't know any of this before we arrived there. After crossing the Mexican border at Tijuana, Jennifer and I continued heading south, putting as much distance as we could between ourselves and the vengeful Marty J. Pretzel Jr. After Mexico, we drove through all the little countries of Central America, and then on into Colombia, Peru, Bolivia, Paraquay and Brazil. Sharing new and exotic experiences, plus the *frisson* of danger, brought us closer together and our relationship developed a greater maturity and depth of feeling. In fact, bit by bit, I found myself feeling really rather soppy about her. I remember verbatim the cooing words that passed between us as we lay under the mosquito netting in our hammocks, a precaution against anacondas and creepy-crawlies, in the Amazon rain forest near Rio Branco.

'I say, old sausage,' I said having decided to declare my feelings to her, 'you're a damned good egg.'

'Lucky, you're a brick,' she replied. 'Now get some shut-eye, and we'll have a cosy in the morning.'

***

Although interesting to visit, none of the countries we had passed through had appealed to us as places to settle, but we had high hopes of Argentina. After all, Buenos Aires has a Harrods, the only one in the world outside Knightsbridge. However, it proved to be but a pale imitation of the real thing, an observation that applied to life as a whole in Buenos Aires at the time of our visit. The country was under the rule of a Junta of generals who were conducting a no-holds-barred war against a bunch of left-wing urban guerrillas. Fear stalked the streets and we were happy to cut short our stay and continue heading south.

One thousand five hundred miles further on, having traversed the Pampas and the whole of Patagonia, we came to Punta Arenas in Tierra del Fuego. An unprepossessing collection of makeshift shacks, its claim to fame is that it is the world's southernmost settlement, little more than a stone's throw from the Antarctic ice cap. We had literally reached the end of the earth. Over coffee after a slap-up scoff in the town's leading hotel, emboldened, I suspect, by the excellent bottle of Concha y Toro Merlot that had accompanied dinner, I suggested to Jennifer that the time had come for us to put down roots.

'What in this dump?' she responded. 'Not on your nelly.'

'No, no, not in Punta Arenas. In the Falklands.'

'Where?'

'The Falkland Islands. They're ours, a British colony in the South Atlantic, about 300 miles out to sea.'

'Do they speak English?'

'Sort of. More in the manner of New Zealand than New Bond Street, I believe.'

'Oh, I had great fun in New Zealand. Such charming, homely people. And all those sheep. Let's give the Falklands a whirl.'

'Cheers,' I responded, toasting our future in Chilean vino tinto.

'I think we'll both be very happy there.'

★★★

We settled in Stanley, the islands' capital, a settlement of about a thousand souls that straggles along the shores of a well-protected natural harbour. We rented a typical Stanley house, a white wooden building with a steeply pitched roof made of sheets of galvanised iron painted the colour of sherbet limes. When it rained, as it did frequently and fiercely, it sounded like a calypso band was playing in the attic.

The front door led straight into a sizeable sitting room, furnished like an Ideal Home of the Macmillan years, with fussy fabrics and flying ducks. A staircase in the corner of the room led upstairs to the bedroom and bathroom. But the heart of the house was the kitchen-cum-breakfast room, which was kept toast-warm by an Aga-like peat burning stove. It was there that we spent most of our time, with the BBC World Service, our link with the outside world, as a companion. It was a simple home, but we were happy as hamsters.

Out at the back, surrounded by a chest-high wooden palisade, was an extensive yard with wooden sheds and pens that had once housed rabbits and chickens to provide some dietary diversity from lamb.

Some people just don't know when they're lucky!

I found work on a farm close to Stanley. It was outdoor manly work that soon put the apples back in my cheeks, rounding up the sheep for dipping, distributing winter feed and just keeping an eye on the woolly blighters. A lot of rude remarks are made about sheep. Of course they're not exactly a flock of Einsteins, but they are stolid, safe and unostentatious creatures to work with, which made them an agreeable change from Robert Maxwell and the Village People. Because the farms are very big, the terrain rugged, not unlike the Highlands of Scotland, and roads mostly non-existent, the Falklands shepherds get around on scrambler bikes with chunky cross-country tyres. Haring up and down the hills on a motorbike was sporting good fun, though pretty knackering for the sheep dogs.

Jennifer was taken on as a barmaid in the pub, and it was through her acquaintances that we built up a social life. She struck up a friendship with a certain Mrs Busybody, without realising that she was Stanley's foremost gossip-monger and curtain-twitcher. Mrs Busybody was for ever inviting her round for a *smoko*, the local term for a cup of tea and a natter. After a while, Jennifer became wary of her relentless probings, fearing that she might let slip something that would give a clue to my real identity. She also became weary of Mrs Busybody's bitchy tittle-tattle. So she started to skip the smokos, making excuses about being busy of having a headache, or whatever.

Then a customer in the pub let on that Mrs Busybody's rumour machine was focused on us, spreading the word that not only were we living in sin but that I was an actor, and a failed one too, who had fled Hollywood because I was turned down for the part of James Bond. Jennifer was furious and I had physically to restrain her from going round and knocking Mrs Busybody's block off with a rolling pin. Actually, it struck me that the old bat had done us a bit of a favour, having invented a much better cover story than anything I could have thought up.

In many ways the kelpers are more British than today's inhabitants of the British Isles, holding on to traditional British traits and values. They're hard-working, straight-

forward, common-sensical and honest. The local constabu-
lary in their honeysuckle-decked police station had more
trouble with aphids than criminals.

They're deeply patriotic and hold the royal family in great
affection. Witnessing the outpouring of these sentiments
during the celebrations of the wedding between Prince
Charles and Diana Spencer taking place 8,000 miles away
made us feel proud to be living amongst them. The kelpers
are made of the same sterling stuff as Mrs Thatcher, my own
political pin-up.

As their revelries that day revealed to us, the kelpers are no
kill-joys when it comes to partying. All the usual pretexts,
such as birthdays, anniversaries, Christmas and New Year are
taken full advantage of, but it was a surprise to discover that
London's Lord Mayor's Day is a public holiday there. Any
old excuse, as Shakespeare put it. Making moonshine was a
favourite pastime amongst our little group of friends, their
hospitality featuring a daunting variety of unfamiliar bever-
ages made from local fruits and plants. I became particularly
fond of a glass or two of diddle dee gin – any more rendering
me temporarily blind and insane. I later learned that it was
also most efficacious for stripping paint, unblocking drains
and de-coking the engine blocks of the ubiquitous Land
Rovers.

At the root of the kelpers' predilection for partying is the
absence of television. There people make their own fun, and
whatever form it takes – a dance, a whist drive, a darts match,
a picnic – they have a whale of a time. They're also avid film
fans, the weekly showings in the Town Hall and the Parish
Hall being packed to capacity. I have many happy memories
of these occasions, but they are besmirched by my recollec-
tions of our last such evening. As usual, we turned up without bothering to enquire what was showing that night. A hush
came over the audience as we appeared, and all eyes were cast

in our direction as the usherette led us to a couple of reserved seats in the centre of the front row. No sooner had we sat down, than Mrs Busybody strode to the front of the hall and announced that there was something special about tonight's film. It starred one of Stanley's own – me. It was – *Can't Stop The Music.*

Jennifer was adamant that she saw me in a couple of shots, but I wasn't so sure. Everybody else thought I was one of the Village People, though opinion was divided as to which one. Not that it mattered. It was the discrepancy between the figures poncing around in sequinned fancy dress, and the standing I had enjoyed, *grace á* Mrs Busybody, as the man who almost played the dashing James Bond that made me a laughing stock. People were giggling behind their hands, and I even heard some stinker remark that I was probably a danger to the sheep in my care. My reputation was in tatters.

Back at the ranch, Jennifer apologised profusely, explaining that she had been a bit loose-lipped in the early days of her friendship with Mrs Busybody. Yes, she had somewhat exaggerated my career as an actor, but with the best intentions to bolster our social position. I didn't blame her. Anyway, the harm was done. We drowned our sorrows in diddle dee gin and when the bottle was empty moved on to tea berry schnapps, another kelper tipple that I suspect Squiffy Marchmain would have taken quite a shine to. It was an unfortunate cocktail, that made me even more maudlin in my cups.

'Chin up, Lucky,' said Jennifer. 'Remember tomorrow is the first day of the rest of your life.'

★★★

It was already mid-afternoon when I got up on the first day of the rest of my life, feeling, I admit, more than a little frayed at the edges.

Drawing the curtains, I was astonished at the sight that greeted me.

'I say, old sausage,' I called to Jennifer who was still in bed and shielding her eyes with a pillow, 'the harbour's full of warships.'

'Rubbish,' she replied. 'You're hallucinating. I warned you about mixing your drinks.'

Not entirely believing my own eyes, I went downstairs and peeked out of the front door. To my amazement, the street was full of foreign soldiers and there were blue and white flags fluttering everywhere. I shut the door and scuttled back to the bedroom.

'They've landed,' I shouted excitedly, bringing on a stonking great headache.

'I suppose they're green, with eyes on stalks?' replied Jennifer mockingly.

'Not aliens, you twit. The Argentines. They've invaded. The street is full of soldiers with guns.'

'Don't worry, the British Army will sort them out,' she muttered. Pulling the eiderdown over her head, she disappeared under the bedclothes.

It dawned on me that Jennifer was prophetic, and I wished I could disappear so easily. Her words haunted me. She was right. Mrs Thatcher wouldn't let the islanders down. She'd send the lot – the Navy, the Air Force, the Marines, the Infantry, the Cavalry and the Brigade of Guards, including my old regiment. My old muckers would recognise me immediately. There would be no hiding my identity from them. Soon as they showed up, I would be on my way to chokey.

★★★

In the early weeks of the occupation, things weren't too bad. The Argentine solders were scrupulously courteous to the kelpers, in accordance with their orders. In fact, the Argies bent over backwards to win our hearts and minds. Just a few days after the invasion we were visited by a high-ranking English-speaking officer of the occupying forces.

'Want to buy a television set at a special price?' he said, standing on the doorstep.

I was rather taken aback, partly because one doesn't expect such spivy conduct from a smartly dressed senior soldier, but also because there was no more redundant item in the Falklands than a TV.

'There's nothing to watch,' said Jennifer, giving expression to my thoughts.

'Haven't you read the communiqué? We're installing a new transmitter that can receive signals from the mainland.' the caller replied. 'Now that you have been liberated, you will enjoy the amenities of modern life. A consignment of television sets has just been delivered to the islands. The government has decided that they will be sold to islanders at a heavily subsidised price, as a token of our goodwill. It's almost a give-away.'

'Thank you, but I don't think so,' I said. To my mind the absence of television was one of the blessings of the Falklands' way of life, and I was appalled to hear that the Argentines intended to foist all the horrors of modernity upon the islands.

'Oh yes we do,' said Jennifer. 'We're not missing out on a bargain. We'll take one.'

As ever, Jennifer had her way. But her enthusiasm for the new device didn't last long, since the only programmes available were two hours-a-day of Spanish language soap operas. Since almost none of the kelpers could speak the lingo, everyone reckoned that the Argies had pulled a fast one. Being invaded was tiresome enough, but being conned out of their cash added insult to injury.

Another source of friction was the edict to drive on the

right. The law-abiding kelpers were bamboozled by the instruction to drive on the wrong side of the road, while the Argentine Army drivers, often mere teenagers, were perplexed by the traffic markings appropriate to driving on the left. Motoring became like dodgem cars, fuelling the growing hostility of the islanders against the invaders and anyone fraternising with them.

Initially the mood amongst the Argentine troops was almost festive. Most of them were college-age conscripts who were proud as punch to participate in the making of history, which was also a lot more fun than hanging around the barracks. And it wasn't even dangerous; well, not until the British bombed Stanley airport after which, reminded of their mortality, their mood became markedly more sombre.

The approaching British task force wasn't the only dispiriting factor; cold, damp and hunger were also taking their tolls. Winter was setting in, and a Falklands winter is a formidably blustery, chilly and damp affair. So the soldiers built bonfires. However, the Falklands are almost treeless and wood is a scarce commodity and pretty soon all the driftwood and scavengable bits of derelict timber had been used up. At which point, they moved in on our dwellings. Every night a section of fencing, part of a garden shed, or even planks from the house itself would disappear.

One night I caught them at it. Hearing footsteps in the back garden, I crept downstairs, opened the back door and pointed a powerful torch in the direction of the noise. I pressed the button and the beam slapped a soldier full in the face. He halted, dazzled, like a rabbit in a car headlight. There was something uncannily familiar about the fellow. He looked uncannily like Enrico, Jennifer's body-builder friend from Muscle Beach who had forged my Green Card in California.

'Enrico? Is that really you?' I spluttered.

'Turn off the goddamn flashlight, will you,' he replied, shielding his eyes with his arm. I recognised the sing-song Latino voice. It *was* Enrico.

'Come inside out of the rain,' I said. 'How about a nice cup of tea?'

'Sure thing, amigo,' he said, putting down our wooden garden bench that he was carrying off in his arms.

We went into the warm kitchen and I put on the kettle. Jennifer, roused by the rumpus, joined us a couple of minutes later and there was an emotional reunion. I was rather taken aback, having never realised how well they knew each other. In fact, I wondered what she had been up to all those days that I had been hard at work at film school. But that was all in the past, I told myself, and, as they say, what the eye doesn't see the heart doesn't grieve over.

Enrico explained that by coincidence he had been back in Argentina on holiday when the mobilisation for the Malvinas, as he called the Falklands, had been instigated. As a reservist with English language skills he had been drafted into active service without so much as a by-your-leave. He told us about the hardships he and his men were suffering because of the brass-monkey weather and their poor provisions. In his bedraggled state, it was hard not to feel sorry for them, even though they were the enemy. Kind-hearted Jennifer went so far as to suggest that he should pop in for a warming cup of tea any time he was in the neighbourhood, an invitation to which he took liberal advantage.

We saw rather a lot of Enrico in the following weeks. He was forever calling on one pretext or another. Jennifer raided my wardrobe to provide him and his friends with warmer clothes, several jumpers, a pair of gloves and most of my socks being handed over to the enemy. The quid pro quo, was that the night-time depredations of our timber stopped. But I was becoming less concerned about losing fence-posts than about losing Jennifer. Day by day the dirty dog's flirtatious behaviour became more and more flagrant. And she lapped it up! Gussie or Boy would have taken a horse-whip to the four-letter fellow, but I stayed cool as a cucumber, biding my moment.

***

We followed the progress of the British task force on the BBC World Service and so had a pretty good idea of the way the war was going. Over the radio we learned of the sinking of the Belgrano, the landings in Falkland Sound and the British victories at Goose Green and Darwin about 60 miles to the west. Then the nightly bombardment of the Argentine positions around Stanley started, and it was obvious that the British forces were closing in on the town. And every step they took shortened my life of liberty.

I was in the kitchen sitting at the scrubbed pine breakfast table when Jennifer and Enrico returned from the General Store where they had gone together to do the shopping. She maintained that having an officer from the occupying forces escort her around town was a sensible precaution against unwanted attentions from conscripts. I agreed and even encouraged her to take him along whenever she went out, declining to accompany her myself because of the embarrassment I still felt about the screening of *Can't Stop The Music*.

Trilling with laughter, she pulled an apple out of the shopping bag and handed it to me. I handed her the piece of paper lying on the table in front of me.

She fell silent as she read the letter, her brow furrowing as her eyes moved down the page.

'That bitch. How dare she,' Jennifer exploded.

'Who do you mean?'

'Mrs Busybody, of course.'

'How do you know its her? It's unsigned.'

'Of course it's her. Who else could have written that bile. And it reeks of Palmolive soap. She always smells of Palmolive,' she said sniffing the paper.

'What's going on?' demanded Enrico.

'I've received an anonymous letter informing me that my companion, Jennifer, is having an affair with one of the enemy,' I told him. 'That means you. The letter also refers to the fate of women collaborators after the liberation of France in 1945.'

'Huh? But that was years ago,' responded the Argentine body-builder, whose brain power was inverse to his brawn.

'All sorts of humiliations were meted out. Shaving heads was commonplace. Tarring and feathering not unknown. The same could happen to poor Jennifer.'

'Hey, *hombre*. Today there are human rights.'

'And responsibilities. They're straight-forward folk the kelpers, with a strong sense of right and wrong behaviour. And having an affair with one of the enemy definitely falls in the latter category.'

'What affair?' exploded Jennifer. 'How dare you say that anything is going on between us!'

I had expected her to come out fighting, and had decided not to respond in kind.

'I haven't said anything of the sort, old sausage. But someone thinks otherwise,' I replied calmly, pointing at the letter.

'It's that bloody Mrs Busybody. I could strangle her.'

'Hey, why don't I just ask my *amigos* in the *Buzos Tacticos* to fix her case,' chipped in Enrico, demonstrating what he had in mind by running an outstretched index finger across his neck.

'No! No!' I said emphatically. 'Murder will make matters worse. We'll all end up facing war crimes charges when the British arrive.'

'The British will never defeat us. The Malvinas belong to Argentina.'

'The British are about to attack Stanley. Tell me, how are a bunch of half-trained, freezing, famished, sleep-starved conscripts, with clapped-out equipment, going to defeat a professional army? Do you really believe you're going to win?'

Enrico thought long and hard, contorting his face as he confronted the cold facts.

'You are right, *amigo*. We will lose,' he muttered with resignation. 'It should not be so, but it will be.'

I nodded solemnly, suggesting sympathy with his sentiments. 'I think you'll be surprised to learn that I agree with you. In fact, we're fighting on the same side.'

'What do you mean?' said Enrico, with a confused countenance. Jennifer looked puzzled too.

'I have something to tell you both. This will come as a shock to you too, Jennifer,' I said gazing fixedly at her, emulating the way a snake-charmer controls a cobra with his eyes. I was trying to make sure that she didn't scupper my story.

'I am agent 365 of the Argentine Secret Service,' I announced.

'You are a spy for us?' exclaimed Enrico incredulously. Jennifer drew breath and gawped at me open-mouthed. But she kept silent and didn't let the side down.

'That's right.'

'What do you do for us?' asked Enrico suspiciously.

'I was sent here by the Junta to report on the movements of British military personnel in preparation for the liberation of the islands.'

'How do you make your reports?' he asked.

I indicated the radio telephone that was a standard piece of equipment in every kelper home.

'You're lying,' snapped Enrico. 'Those machines can't reach the mainland.'

'Quite right. But they can reach a submarine sitting on the surface just outside territorial waters. That's how we communicated,' I replied imperturbably. 'But now your behaviour with Jennifer has compromised my position. She is accused of collaboration with the enemy. The British must know that somebody was acting as an Argentine agent on the islands, and thanks to you the finger is pointing firmly at us. When they get here I'll be arrested and probably go to jail. A British prison is no holiday, but I wouldn't like to be in your shoes.'

'What do you mean?'

'What do you imagine is going to happen to you when the Junta learns that you blew the cover of their man in Stanley?'

'But I ain't done nothin'. I just hung loose with the *chiquita*,' protested Enrico, sounding surprised and rattled.

'Tell that to the secret police when they catch up with you.'

'Holy Maria,' wailed Enrico, 'they are monsters those people.' Now there was panic in his voice.

'No, no. Much nastier,' I said, stoking his paranoia. I was well-aware of the awesome reputation of the notorious secret police death squads.

'What can I do? They will torture me and kill me. I don't want to die,' moaned Mr Universe, starting to sob.

'Now pull yourself together, old chap,' I said brusquely. 'Just do as I say, and maybe we'll all be tickety-boo. . .'

***

The two-day crossing from the Falklands to Puerto Madryn in southern Argentina in the *Canberra* was a pleasant cruise. Enrico, Jennifer and I shared a first class cabin, that had been vacated expeditiously without protest by other Argentine prisoners of war when Enrico had told them about my contacts with the secret police.

Jennifer cut a somewhat implausible figure as an Argentine conscript, but trussed up in a big baggy great coat with a tin hat on her head and a scarf covering all but her eyes, she got away with it. Enrico had worked fast and effectively to fulfil my instructions, getting hold of the uniforms we needed and the documents certifying us as members of his unit, which he expertly doctored with his well-honed skills as a forger. By the time the British Army waltzed into town our disguises were ready and we were rounded up with the rest of the prisoners.

On board, Jennifer's attitude towards me underwent a very agreeable transformation. Her initial protests of innocence at the charges in the anonymous letter soon changed to begging for forgiveness for being so foolish as to allow her infatuation with Enrico's biceps to cause our undignified exit from our new home town and life together. She became distinctly tetchy towards the body-builder, who was left in no doubt that she held him fully responsible. In fact, I found myself in the position of keeping them from scratching each others eyes out, while being looked up to by both of them as something of a hero.

We never saw Mrs Busybody again, though for years afterwards Jennifer continued to curse her memory in a most unladylike manner. It is only as she reads these words that Jennifer will learn that it was I who was the author of the letter, written on a piece of paper that I had left overnight wrapped around a bar of Palmolive to implicate Mrs Busybody. An act of deceit, yes, but in a good cause.

Amongst the Argentines I became a war hero. Entirely unprompted, Enrico made it his business to tell all and sundry about my undercover heroism hoping, I suspected, to safeguard himself through association with me. I didn't begrudge him his second-hand glory, though I was somewhat taken aback to be informed upon landing that I was being nominated for a medal for my services to the liberation of the

Malvinas. I needed that sort of razzmatazz like a hole in the head.

Fortunately, Argentina was in turmoil following the rout of the armed forces and it proved easy for us to give Enrico the slip and quietly leg it over the border. It was time to lie doggo again.

8. Trouble in Transylvania

Jennifer took to Marbella like a cat to cream. She was in her element amongst the boats and bistros, declaring that she hadn't been so happy since those heady days in Cap Ferrat. We settled in at my modest apartment, which was just as I had left it though everything was covered in a layer of dust and there were cobwebs in the kitchen. My bank balance was also just as I had left it – empty.

'I'm afraid that we're in a bit of a pickle moneywise, old sausage,' I told Jennifer when I got home from a chat with the bank manager. 'Basically, we're skint.'

'Alright, I'll get a job,' she replied pluckily.

'Me too,' I declared, inspired by her thought.

'Oh no, you won't, Lucky. I haven't come through all this to have you spotted by some ex-pat who puts the police on to you. You're going to keep your head down. We'll spend the evenings at home together.'

'But what am I going to do all day?'

'What did you do before?'

'I used to go for drives and chat with the locals.'

'Girls?'

'Mostly men.'

'Where?'

'In bars, of course. My favourite watering hole was the *Sol y Sombra* in Ronda, where. . .'

'Hold on, I'm not going out to work so you can hang around in bars all day. If I'm the bread winner, you'll have to look after the house.'

Thus began my brief career as housewife.

***

Jennifer found a job as a waitress in a restaurant in Estepona run by an English couple from Borehamwood. But it proved impossible to make ends meet on her earnings and we found ourselves slipping into debt. The solution was obvious. I would have to go back to work for Maxwell. Jennifer was adamantly against me having anything to do with him, but the mounting pile of bills argued the other way. Maxwell owed me a substantial sum in respect of outstanding salary and expenses for which I had not been reimbursed, more than enough to clear the slate. Another consideration on my mind was the cleaning, cooking and ironing; the sooner I could afford a maid to do all that sort of stuff the better.

Without mentioning it to Jennifer, I dialled Maxwell's top secret personal hot line. A voice demanded some special code words, which I provided, and seconds later the big man himself was on the line.

'Where the fuck have you been?' growled Maxwell. He continued in his customary foul-mouthed vein for at least ten minutes, the brief pauses in his blusterings and threats being filled by my abject apologies. In fact, I did feel a bit guilty about walking out on him and my sincerity must have got through to him, because all of a sudden there was an abrupt change of tone and vocabulary and he started laying on the charm. He said how much he had missed my company and services and how delighted he was that I would be working for him again. It was time to let bygones be bygones. Then he told me to start packing because we would shortly be going hunting with President Nicolae Ceausescu of Romania. It was an offer, he made clear, I couldn't refuse.

***

The visit to Romania was different to the other trips I did with Maxwell, or on his behalf, because Ceausescu's volume of biography had already appeared in the *Leaders of the World* series, raising a couple of questions I didn't dare ask. What did Maxwell hope to get out of it? And why did he want me along?

The morning after our telephone conversation, a large brown manila envelope thudded on to my Marbella doormat. Dressed in my Harrods maroon and navy Guards-stripe pyjamas, I opened it at once. It contained a copy of Ceausescu's biography, an airline ticket and some hand-written instructions. I was told to rendezvous with Maxwell in Paris in three day's time, from whence we would proceed to Bucharest and then to a hunting lodge in Transylvania. In the meantime, I was to read the book from cover to cover. It sounded like a lot more fun than doing the shopping.

I strolled into the kitchen where Jennifer was arranging the breakfast things on the table. She was fetchingly, some might say provocatively, attired in a pink baby-doll nightie from Frederick's of Hollywood, a discovery of our days in Los Angeles.

'Guess what?' I said brandishing the envelope.

'It's from bloody Maxwell, isn't it?'

'How did you know?'

'Have you been in touch with him?'

'Errr, yes,' I confessed.

'Oh Lucky, why? You know I've never hankered after the things most girls expect from men, the flat in Chelsea, the house in Gloucestershire, the big BMW. What I want is you, and I want you around *here*, not in some far flung corner of the world.'

'It's the only way to get him to pay me what he owes me. Then we'll be able to make ends meet, old sausage.'

'Well, just make sure it is the last time, Lucky. Where's he sending you now, Timbuktu?'

'No, no. Just Transylvania.'

Jennifer stared at me. Her complexion was suddenly ashen and her features were locked in shock.

'You're not going there,' she declared categorically. 'It's out of the question.'

Not again, I thought. We had just established that we needed the money. What's more, now he knew I had returned, like the prodigal son, to my roost, he could tip off the police and I would end up in chokey.

'It's only for a weekend. I won't have to hang around for ages, because he's already published Ceausescu's biography.'

'Then why does he want you along?'.

'I'm not sure. He says he wants my company. The trip seems to be a sort of jolly, not a work thing.'

'No, no. It's far too dangerous.'

'Dangerous? Romania is far from dangerous if you're the guests of the President. It's a police state. They'll be security guards everywhere. Crossing the road here is more hazardous.'

'I'm talking about the undead.'

'The *what*?'

'Oh Lucky, for once in your life think carefully about what you're doing,' she implored. 'Who is Transylvania famous for?'

'Illie Nastase?'

'Dracula, that's who! Suppose *you* became a vampire's titbit. I'd never forgive you.'

'Oh come off it, old sausage. That vampire stuff is a load of bunkum. A bit of fun for teenage filmgoers who like to be frightened. Look, you don't think Maxwell would be going if there was a threat from vampires do you?'

I spoke forthrightly and ostensibly with complete conviction, but, in fact her words were troubling me. Although I didn't let on, my bravado was to reassure myself as well as her.

'Maybe you're right. Maxwell certainly looks after number one,' she replied sullenly. Then she brightened.

'Do you remember Agatha at Cap Ferrat? She knows all about things supernatural. I'm going to call her and ask her advice.'

Jennifer finished her cup of coffee, stood up and flounced to the 'phone in the sitting room.

Sipping a cup of Twinings English breakfast tea and munching slices of toast liberally topped with Frank Cooper's Coarse Cut Original Oxford Marmalade, I perused the book Maxwell had instructed me to read. It was a handsomely produced volume entitled *Nicolae Ceausescu: Builder of Modern Romania and International Statesman,* with a royal blue cover and gold lettering. But everything else about it was decidedly naff. The colour portrait of him on the front cover was so flagrantly retouched that he resembled a Madame Tussaud waxwork. It was an insipid face; a button nose; baby cheeks, twinkly-winkly eyes; crinkly hair; the small mouth coyly tweaked into a twee smile. It looked like an old-fashioned publicity picture for a brand of toothpaste.

I skimmed through the volume, pausing every few pages to get the measure of what I was missing. It was choc-a-bloc with references to dialectical materialism and other such twaddle, bringing back ghastly memories of Castro's re-education school in Cuba. I slammed it closed. A trip to Transylvania was one thing, but I wasn't going to squander my time reading that rubbish.

Jennifer returned carrying the note-pad that sat by the 'phone. Her cheeks were moist and her eyes a little bloodshot, indicating that she had been blubbing. But now she was smiling.

'Chin up, old sausage,' I said encouragingly.

'Agatha's given me a list of everything you'll need to take,' she said between sniffles.

'Let's hear it then.'

'Garlic is vital. Vampires are repelled by garlic. You peel a clove and rub it on the door and the windows to stop them coming in. Rub it on your body too, especially round your neck and under your armpits.'

'Armpits?'

'That's what she told me. Oh Lucky, just do what she says. She knows what she's talking about. You will, won't you? You promise?'

'Alright, I promise,' I said.

'You'll need fishing nets. I'll pop down to Puerto Banus for some this morning.'

'We're going hunting, not trawling.'

'To drape over windows and doors. Agatha says they're a very effective deterrent because vampires are afraid of getting tangled up in them. Then there's incense, holy water and candles that have been blessed by a priest. That ought to keep them away. But just in case one gets into your room you need some holly leaves to scatter around your bed and a crucifix, plus a wooden stake, a mallet, a mirror, a powerful electric torch and a crowbar.'

'What's the crowbar for?'

'Prizing open coffins, I think.'

'We're not going grave robbing. We're guests of the head of state,' I protested plaintively.

'You know what your trouble is,' Jennifer replied rounding on me with exasperation. 'You're a know-all. Agatha's the expert on vampires. She says take a crowbar. Why don't you just follow her advice?'

So I took a crowbar. I'd learned the hard way that life is a lot more agreeable if I don't argue with Jennifer when she really has her mind set on something.

***

I carried the large black leather Gladstone bag full of vampire prophylactics on to the plane as hand luggage, having promised Jennifer not to let my equipment out of my sight. All except the crowbar, which went in the hold so as not to trigger the airport metal detectors. I didn't relish trying to explain to a French security guard at Charles de Gaulle that I was carrying it just in case I had to prise open a vampire's coffin.

While Maxwell located our seats, I struggled to put the heavy bag into an overhead locker. A *Tarom Airlines* stewardess, wearing a badge reading Magda, came to my assistance. Magda had the up-lift of a fork-lift truck, as well as the figure, and the bag soared into place. I thanked her and sat down next to Maxwell. He was eating, as usual, working his way through the stuffed baguette he'd bought in the departure lounge.

'Done your homework?' he demanded, his mouth brimming with sandwich, a dribble of mayonnaise wending its way down his chin. It was a disgusting spectacle.

'It's unreadable. It's a pile of Marxist gobbledy-gook and sycophantic tosh, proclaiming Ceausescu as the best thing since sliced bread.'

'He's over-the-moon about it,' said Maxwell chortling. 'That's why I've been invited to go hunting with him. Sort of a thank you present. Which sounds like a promising business opportunity.'

'How?'

'Romania is big in forest products.'

'Such as squirrels?'

'Trees, you dick-head, from which you get pulp for newsprint. My newspapers need an awful lot of newsprint these days.'

'Is that why you published Ceausescu's biography?'

'Of course. Nobody reads that bull-shit. There are no

bookshop sales. The only purchaser is the Romanian government which gives them away as freebies. Even those orders
don't cover my costs. But that's not the point. It's part of a
much bigger game.'

'Where do I fit in? You've already published the book, you
don't need me to hang around waiting for Ceausescu's signature.'

'It's vital that I make a good impression. You must understand how important that is,' he said emphatically. 'You see
I'd already promised Joseph the weekend off before Ceausescu's invitation arrived.'

'Who's Joseph?'

'My butler.'

'So what?'

'You're his stand-in. Your tail-coat and the rest of the kit
are in my suitcase.'

'You're joking. I agreed to work for you as your special rep-
resentative, not your manservant. The Lucans are Lords, not
butlers.'

'You'll do it my way, sunshine, unless you want a one-way
ticket to Wormwood Scrubs. Old Nicolae's going to be
jealous as hell when I tell him that I've got a genuine English
aristocrat for a butler. He'll want one too, mark my words.'

'What do I have to do?' I enquired resignedly. After all it
was only for a weekend.

'Fetch drinks. Polish my shoes. Iron the newspaper. That
sort of thing. And look fittingly servile and respectful.
Nothing too arduous.'

'Do I have to eat in the kitchen? I mean, mix with the
Romanian staff?'

'Well, I doubt that Nicolae and Elena will be happy having
my butler joining us at table for dinner.'

'I suppose not. Listen, this may sound a bit silly to you, but
Jennifer, my girlfriend, is very worried about me getting

bitten by a vampire. Apparently Transylvania is where they come from and a friend who knows about the supernatural has told her that there are still some around.'

'Crap,' said Maxwell gruffly.

'Well, I've promised her to be on my guard,' I said.

'If you're worried about fucking vampires, you belong in a loony bin,' said Maxwell. 'Wait till you meet Elena Ceausescu. Now there's a real-life monster with fangs.'

★★★

A long black Soviet bloc limousine, a sort of biscuit-box on wheels, was waiting to meet us at Otopeni, Bucharest's airport. The driver, Valentin, looked decidedly sinister in the long black leather coat of the sort worn by the Gestapo in war films. He greeted us in excellent English, it being immediately obvious that he and Maxwell were well acquainted.

'Any problems? It's in good shape, I hope,' said Maxwell gazing at the mysterious object draped in tarpaulins and secured with ropes, sitting on the trailer of the large lorry parked behind the limousine.

'Everything's fine,' replied Valentin. 'We picked it up from the ship at Constanta yesterday. I supervised the unloading personally, as you instructed.'

'Good man,' said Maxwell. He produced his wallet and pulled out a couple of $100 dollar bills, handing them to Valentin. A king's ransom in these parts. Whatever Maxwell was up to, Valentin was doing very nicely out of it.

★★★

Maxwell fired question after question about the situation in Romania as we drove towards Transylvania. According to Valentin, who seemed remarkably well-informed for a chauffeur, everything in the garden was rosy. An epic modernisation programme was underway in Bucharest. Oh, there had

been complaints from some reactionary elements who had
tried to impede the march of progress, protesting about their
homes being knocked down. But the Securitate had sorted
them out. In the countryside too, systematisation, modernisation and civilisation were advancing, destroying the breeding grounds of bourgeois liberalism, as Valentin put it. It
gradually became clear that what he was saying in Marxist jar-
gon, was that pretty traditional villages were being bulldozed
and their inhabitants rehoused in high rise apartment blocks.
'Easier to keep an eye on them there,' Valentin explained, 'for
their own protection, of course.'

***

The Romanian countryside looked quaint and gently undu-
lating, like Wiltshire without the hedgerows. Spring was coming. New shoots were turning the fields from ploughed earth
to swathes of green, while the bare branches of the trees were
specked with buds and catkins. People were stirring too,
sturdy peasants in Homburgs or head shawls driving horse-
drawn carts and flocks of sheep along the road. Humans and
animals scattered before us at arrogant blasts from Valentin's
klaxon.

The highway itself was patched and pitted, and every time
we hit a rut the big black machine grumbled and hiccuped
and lurched its passengers hither and thither. It was more like
a journey by stage coach than a ride in a modern motor car.
But then the whole countryside was a step back in time. Back
to the days of Dracula? I wondered.

After about an hour, we reached the foothills of the
Carpathians and the road became more tortuous. Soon we
were in the midst of the mountains, steep-sided, rock-
faced, tusks that offered scant hospitality to man or beast.
And then the landscape changed again, and we were in a
craggy, wooded plateau that lived up to the name Transyl-

vania. Rounding a bend, a higgledy-piggledy medieval fortress perched atop a sheer rocky outcrop loomed into view.

'The castle of Vlad Tepes,' announced Valentin. 'You call him Dracula. For us he is a national hero.'

'A hero? He was a vampire,' I said bewilderedly.

'Perhaps he was. He was also a great warrior, fighting the Turks. He used to impale his enemies on stakes. They say that is how to kill a vampire.'

'Do you still have vampires?' I asked.

'Some people say that our president and his wife are vampires. Of course, the Securitate deal with them. But then some people say that the Securitate themselves are vampires. In which case we have many, many vampires.' He laughed, but I didn't understand the punch-line.

'Who are the Securitate?' I asked.

'The secret police,' said Maxwell. 'The stewardess you met on the flight over. She was one of them.'

'How do you know?'

'She wasn't aboard for her looks or her charm was she?'

'He is right,' said Valentin. 'The Securitate are everywhere. In this car, for instance.'

'You are Securitate?'

'Of course.'

'What's the difference between a rock musician and a pig?' said Maxwell, changing the subject.

'Huh?' responded Valentin.

'A pig won't stay up all night to shag a rock musician,' cackled Maxwell.

'I don't understand,' said Valentin.

'It's a joke,' said Maxwell. 'Maybe you'll get this one. Two cannibals are having dinner together. The guest says "Your wife sure makes good soup." "Yeah, but I miss her," his friend replies.'

He roared with laughter. Valentin tittered too.

'I know a Romanian joke,' he said. 'What's Dracula's favourite dog?'

'A poodle,' responded Maxwell playfully. Valentin smiled slyly.

'Wrong. A bloodhound,' he replied darkly.

Maxwell liked that so much he followed up with his favourite. 'Hey, do you know the one about the parking warden who gets shagged by a camel. . .'

I sat silent on the back seat clutching my bag full of vampire deterrents. I was feeling more and more grateful for Jennifer's precautions.

***

Ceausescu's Transylvanian hunting lodge was something of a disappointment. I'd been expecting a brooding, gothic castle whose giant portal would be opened by a sinister crook-backed manservant called Igor. In fact, it was a newish-looking, Swiss-style chalet with a gently pitched roof with wide eaves sheltering a wooden balustraded balcony at the base of the building. It was set in a flat, grassy forest clearing surrounded by pine trees. Half-a-dozen limousines and some military and police vehicles were lined up on one side and beyond them was parked a white 4-seater helicopter. Plainly our hosts had already arrived.

The front door opened and a short, stout, middle-aged woman appeared on the porch, a pair of Labradors at her heels. Her Charolais-coloured skirt and jacket, and the baggy red and brown blouse exaggerated her dumpiness. She had a prominent bobble-tipped nose, dark eyebrows, high forehead and chestnut-coloured hair with the coppery aura of cheap hair-dye. She was screaming at us in Romanian, her unprepossessing features screwed into a picture of pure venom. Too bad it wasn't Igor, after all.

'Elena Ceausescu,' muttered Maxwell to me as we walked towards the house.

'She says we're late,' Valentin explained.

'Does she always welcome her house guests in this way?' I enquired.

'Oh no,' he replied. 'Usually she's in a bad mood.'

A tall slim man in a dark suit and sunglasses appeared on the balcony behind the harridan.

'Her foreign bodyguard. A very dangerous man,' whispered Valentin under his breath. Not that Elena Ceausescu could have heard since she was still ranting and cursing as loud as her lungs allowed.

There was, I noticed, an awkward, ungainly quality about the bodyguard; and something lingeringly familiar. As we got nearer, I became more certain. Although half-a-dozen years or more had elapsed since we'd last met, he was unmistakable. It was Anwer.

We were led into the house by our bitching hostess. Valentin showed Maxwell and me to our accommodation: his, a suite with a four-poster bed, sitting room and bathroom with an enormous circular bath with inset Jacuzzi nozzles; mine, a little bigger than a shoe-box with bars on the window and a single 40 watt bulb dangling at chest height from the middle of the ceiling. My room was spartanly furnished and decorated, but Maxwell's made Graceland look like a shrine to good-taste. Elena Ceausescu's peasant fantasies of chic and opulence had resulted in a riot of chintz and brocade, bows and swags, and fussy rococo furniture. There were gilt cherubs on the wall either side of the bed-head, a pink Venetian chandelier, and a bunch of plastic dahlias in a light blue Wedgewood-style vase perched on a mock bamboo side table. A matching commode contained a 32 inch television set plus a video recorder. Maxwell, who love to watch anything on TV, switched in on immediately.

'You know *Kojak*?' asked Valentin as Telly Sevallas appeared on the screen. 'It's the Ceausescu's favourite show.'

'How do they get *Kojak* in Transylvania?' I asked naively.

'Their ambassadors in the West are under orders to set video tapes and send them to Bucharest by diplomatic courier. It is one of their most important functions. Then the army brings the tapes to them by helicopter or despatch rider, whichever is quicker. It is the same for *Dallas* and *Dynasty*. They like movies too. *The Great Gatsby* is a great favourite. They watch it again and again.'

'Right, that's enough nattering,' said Maxwell brusquely. He extracted a plastic bag from his suitcase and handed it to me. 'Here's your kit. Now buzz off both of you. I want to watch *Kojak*. . .'

***

Back in my bed-sit I changed into my butler's outfit of black tail coat, matching trousers with satin side-piping, and a starched white shirt with wing-collar. There was a rather unorthodox white three-button waistcoat, a white dickie-bow, white gloves and a white silk scarf with tassels. I felt very comfortable in this get-up, more comfortable I suspected than any butler had a right to be. I looked as if I was off to the opera. Or alternatively, playing the part of the Prince of Darkness in one of those old Hammer Horror films.

There was a gentle knock on the door. It opened and Anwer slipped in quietly, a finger to his lips commanding my silence. He stepped over and enveloped me with both arms in a Russian-style bear-hug. Standing stiffly in his embrace it crossed my mind that he intended to crush me to death on account of our previous fallings out. But, in fact, he was just being friendly.

'I'm glad to see you again,' he whispered, 'you're the closest to a friend I've got in this place.'

'Sounds like we're both in the same boat,' I replied.

'That woman, she is a monster. You've got the help me escape.'

'But why are you here? You're an Arab not a Romanian.'

'My organisation has close ties with Romania. They give us money and arms. In return we provide bodyguards because the Ceausescu's don't even trust their own people. They know that the people hate them. Me too. They are pigs.'

'What?'

'They care only about themselves. She doesn't even love her own children. They treat the staff like scum. We are always hungry, but anyone caught taking the left-overs from their lavish banquets is handed over to the Securitate. They are tyrants.'

'How do you get along? Do you speak Romanian?'

'I was sent on a language course. I speak enough. I must go now or she will miss me. I will talk with you tonight, when they are watching television.' And he was gone.

Poor old Anwer, I reflected, he always seemed to draw the short straw. Despite our differences over the years, I really was pleased to see him. Well, at least there was someone on the staff who wasn't a vampire.

★★★

My next visitor was Maxwell, who had changed out of his travelling clothes and was wearing a grey suit and silk tie. Not bothering to knock, he just strode straight in.

'Get a sodding move on,' he said impatiently. 'We're going to meet the President.'

'Did you know this isn't a butler's suit. It's formal evening dress,' I said, draping the silk scarf round my neck.

'It was all the hire shop had,' he replied grumpily. 'Anyway this bunch won't know the difference. Now come on.'

I followed him through the house and on to the balcony.

Flanked by security guards, Anwer amongst them, stood a short, slight, grey-haired man in a sober suit looking decidedly ill-at-ease as he was berated by Elena. She fell silent as we stepped out and glared at us with loathing.

'Comrade President. Builder of the outstanding stage in the millennia-old existence of the Romanian people. Giant of the Carpathians. Outstanding militant of the international communist and working-class movement and defender of socialism against imperialism, colonialism and neo-colonialism. Creator of the epoch of unprecedented renewal. I greet you,' said Maxwell. Valentin translated his words and Nicolae Ceausescu's reply.

'Hello', said the Romanian head of state.

'Comrade President,' continued Maxwell. 'It is a great honour to be your guest in the peoples' paradise of Romania. I understand that you and your countrymen have embarked on a great and arduous labour of reconstruction. To help with this work I would like to present you with a token of my appreciation of your struggle for socialism.'

Maxwell turned and tramped down the steps from the wooden balcony. He strode over to the mysterious shrouded object that had followed us from the airport and was now standing on the ground in front of the chalet. Taking hold of a dangling rope, he gave a hefty tug. The tarpaulins slid swishingly to the ground, revealing an orange-painted mobile crane. A bemused smile flickered across Ceausescu's lips and he applauded with a few desultory claps. The rest of his entourage followed suit, except Elena, of course. Maxwell bowed and beamed.

★★★

Maxwell and the Ceausescus sat down *a trois* that evening in the dining room. It was decorated in truly awful taste: mock Louis XV furniture with plastic filigree work; an abundance of apricot-tinted mirrors in ornately carved gilded frames; and a gaudy blue and flame-coloured Murano chandelier that hovered over the dining table. Valentin joined them at table, though only in the capacity of interpreter. Anwer and I were also on hand, but we too went hungry, standing behind our respective bosses poised to attend to any whim.

Elena's fancy, during the suckling-pig course, was for her shawl and Anwer was despatched to fetch it. Unfortunately, one of her Labradors had silently sprawled at his feet, so that he tripped over it as he hurried to do her bidding. He lunged headlong knocking over a lamp and reducing a side-table to matchwood. Elena was not amused. She showed this by picking up her plate and throwing it at Anwer, hitting him in the midriff and covering him with pork and gravy. A damn good shot, in fact. But she went a bit far by standing astride him, screaming abuse accusing him of attacking her dog. Nicolae looked on, quietly gnawing some crackling.

'She says he is to go to his room without supper,' said Valentin, distilling her tirade to its main point.

'Looks like he's in the dog-house right and proper,' commented Maxwell, as Anwer slunk out of the room with his tail between his legs. 'With that bitch around,' he muttered to me, *soto voce*, 'it's a dog's life for everyone.'

After dinner, Maxwell and the Ceausescus retired to the sitting room, another kitsch monstrosity, to watch *Kojak*. Having been dismissed for the evening by Maxwell, I made my way to the kitchens where I was served a plate of greasy meatballs and watery cabbage. It was disgusting, worse than Squiffy Marchmain's home-made toad-in-the-hole, and I pushed the plate away after no more than a couple of mouthfuls. No wonder Anwer was looking so gaunt.

***

Back in my bedroom, I removed my tie and sat on the bed

underneath the 40 watt light bulb writing my diary. The door opened and Anwer entered. He had cleaned up his clothes, but was in a filthy mood.

'One of these days, I will kill her,' he spat.

'Don't be silly. That would be suicide.'

'I know, but sometimes she pushes me too far.'

'Are you hungry?'

'Starving.'

'Have this,' I said pulling a Mars Bar out of my luggage.

'Thank you, thank you,' he said his face full of wonder. Ripping the wrapper to shreds, he devoured the chocolate bar in seconds.

'Valentin says that some people say she is a vampire,' I remarked as he sat chewing. He looked puzzled.

'Why do they say that?'

'Because this is Transylvania, the home of Dracula.'

'Is it?' said Anwer, staring at me wide-eyed. 'Nobody ever tells me anything.'

'Have you noticed any of the tell-tale signs?'

'Like what?'

'Pale skin, red eyes, bad breath. . .'

'Bad breath!' he exclaimed, 'her breath stinks like a sewer. And she's often pale and red-eyed, but that's because she stays up late watching *Kojak*.'

'What about fangs, hairy palms, long nails, silent foot-steps. . .'

'A lot of the Securitate look like that. Any of them that tries to bite me, I'll shoot him dead.'

He slapped his thigh and I saw the bulge of a revolver under the loose-fitting jacket.

'What about when you're asleep? It's at night they prowl about.'

'What can I do?' he said, sounding a little panicky. I also was feeling uneasy. My questions had spooked me too.

'Garlic. That's the answer,' I said, opening the big black Gladstone bag and pulling out a long rope of garlic bulbs. 'Vampires hate garlic.'

'What do I do with it?'

'I'll show you.' I said peeling some cloves and handing half to him.

'You rub it round the door and window frames. Like this,' I said, giving a demonstration. 'That's to keep them out of the room. But it may not be strong enough, so you also have to protect your body. You rub the garlic over your skin, especially under your armpits. Eat some too.' As we stood there munching and rubbing the cloves into our skin, I reached into the bag and pulled out a couple of crucifixes. I handed one of them to Anwer.

'What's this?' he said recoiling.

'It's a cross to repel vampires.'

'I'm a Muslim.'

That had me stumped. So I gave him a handful of jasmine joss-sticks instead and told him to light them when he got back to his room.

'Alright,' said Anwer. 'I'll be going now. Thanks for your help.'

'Sleep well,' I whispered, closing the door after him, knowing that probably he would be up all night worrying about being bitten by members of the Securitate. I felt a touch guilty about giving him the willies. But with vampires, it was better to be safe than sorry.

★★★

I rose early, roused by my alarm clock. I shaved, put on my so-called butlers kit and made my way to Maxwell's room. He was already up, dressed in tweed plus-fours, tweed jacket, and tweed cap, like a Scottish laird setting-out for the grouse moor.

'What on earth did they give you for supper?' he demanded, pulling a face.

'Meatballs and cabbage.'

'You stink,' he said with his customary charm. 'You mean garlic and more garlic.'

'A precaution against vampires,' I replied, realising that perhaps I'd overdone it. The thing about garlic, of course, is that you don't smell it on yourself.

'Do belt up about that vampire nonsense,' Maxwell replied irritably.

The house was already bustling with preparations for the great hunting expedition, the staff scurrying in all directions. We made our way to the centre of activity, the large hall by the front door. Anwer was already there, disdainfully keeping an eye on the teeming minions. He looked dreadful, as if he hadn't slept a wink. But he smelt worse, the pungent cocktail of jasmine and garlic wafting from him clawing at my nostrils and setting my teeth on edge. Maxwell pulled a face expressing physical nausea.

'Christ, what a pong.' he exclaimed, coughing as we passed by a yard away.

The sound of shouting came nearer and nearer. A door flew open and Elena, dressed in her hunting gear, a mink coat and high-heeled boots, burst into the room. Spying me and Maxwell, she descended on us, Valentin in tow. Shock and disgust came over her countenance as she came close. She fell silent, took a step backwards and gawped at me. She muttered something to Valentin.

'Madam Ceausescu says that you have been eating garlic. That is strictly forbidden. You will not come hunting. You will stay here.'

'Hold on,' said Maxwell, 'what about your bodyguard? He stinks like a polecat.'

As soon as his words were translated, Anwer was

summoned over. Sheer horror registered on her face as he reached where I was standing.

'Halt,' cried Valentin raising a handkerchief to his nose. 'You reek of garlic. You too will remain behind.'

The first lady of Transylvania leading the way, the assembled company filed out of the front door. Maxwell, whose parting instruction to me was to use the opportunity to flog a set of encyclopaedias to Anwer, disappeared into a waiting limousine with Nicolae and Elena. Soon all the cars had gone and we were alone, save for a few menials.

'You always get me into trouble,' said Anwer sullenly.

'Chin up, old chap. Better a stinker than one of the undead.'

'What?'

'A vampire's victim. I suspect Elena Ceausescu is one of them. You saw the way she recoiled from the garlic? That's just how a vampire would behave. Thank God, I'm going home tomorrow.'

'What about me?' wailed Anwer. 'I'm stuck here.'

'Don't worry, I've got a whole bag of vampire repellents you can have. They'll keep you safe for years, even if you have to go easy on the garlic. And how better to wile away the time than with a good book, or rather a set of books. . .'

★★★

By teatime we were distinctly peckish, having missed out on both breakfast and lunch, and supper the night before too in Anwer's case. We'd tried the kitchen but found it locked, the entire catering staff having decamped with the Ceausescus to pander to their demands.

We lounged about chatting on the steps of the wooden balcony, having fled the oppressive opulence of Elena Ceausescu's taste in interior design. The grass and pine trees didn't amount to much of a view, but it was a damn sight better than all that ormolu and onyx. Across the clearing, gleaming in the sunshine, was Maxwell's mobile crane. I had an idea.

'How far is the nearest village?'

'About five kilometres,' said Anwer.

'Why don't we pop down there for some grub. If we go in the crane we can be back by five o'clock. The hunting party isn't due back till six.'

Anwer looked doubtful. 'If we're not here when she gets back, I'll be in even more trouble.'

'Don't worry, we'll be back in time. And the sooner we get going, the sooner we'll be home.'

★★★

For a short spin, the mobile crane was quite a hoot, though not as much fun as the yellow Morgan I drove in Marbella. It was pretty nippy on the straight stretches, but cornering at speed wasn't a good idea because it was rather top-heavy. After about 20 minutes we emerged from the forest into fields, and soon we were entering a village. It comprised a single narrow street of houses built in the traditional timber-framed style and in a distinctly dilapidated condition. At the end of the street was a square, with a church and an inn.

Anwer leapt down from the crane's cab and bounded into the inn to order our meal. Meanwhile, I parked the crane in the square, in the space between a wooden hay cart and a rusty Dacia. Reversing the long vehicle was tricky, and it was a full five minutes before I joined him inside. I found myself in a large dark room, the gloom interrupted only by the meagre light of a few candles and the glowing embers of a log fire in the big brick fireplace. There were some windows, I noticed, but they were so caked in soot and grime that they admitted little light. Anwer was sitting on a stool at a wooden table on which there was a candle, a large slab of bread and two big steaming bowls of broth. He was horsing the nosh like it was the end of Ramadan. I sat down opposite and tucked in myself.

There was a scuffling behind me that sounded like a rat. I shot a look over my shoulder and found myself face to face with the innkeeper, a cadaverous, stooped figure with dishwater irises who would have made an estimable Hammer Horror film Igor. Panic gripped his features as he gazed at me, the jug and glasses he was carrying slipping from his fingers and crashing to the floor. He took to his heels and fled.

'What's the matter with him?' I asked.

'Who cares?' Anwer replied, being much too pre-occupied with feeding to have paid proper attention to the episode.

We continued eating in silence, relishing the delicious spicy goulash, which was a damn sight superior to the insipid fare I'd been served in the Ceausescu's kitchen. The bread too was hearty and full-flavoured, real staff of life stuff. And I was pleased to be breaking it with Anwer. We had had our differences in the past, but today we were making a damn good team, I mused sentimentally. Little did I suspect how soon our teamwork would be tested.

'We've got company,' said Anwer looking towards the door.

I turned and saw the innkeeper and half-a-dozen companions standing at the far end of the room. More men joined them through the front door as we watched. They were clutching crucifixes and some also had ancient-looking hunting rifles, and all were staring at us. Out in front was a fellow with an enormous torso and a leather apron, who I took to be the village blacksmith. In his hands were a hammer and a wooden stake.

All of a sudden, the innkeeper's paranoid reaction to seeing me made sense.

'It's this butler's costume,' I explained to Anwer. 'It's the way Count Dracula dressed in the old vampire films. They think we're vampires.'

'Not again!' he exclaimed. 'I can't even have a meal in peace when you're around.'

'*Muri Vlad*' yelled the blacksmith, as he charged towards us, stake held high. Anwer drew his revolver and fired a couple of shots into the air. Though just intended as a warning it was a martial masterstroke, bringing down the ceiling's plaster work on the heads of the villagers. A large chunk of masonry bounced off the blacksmith's bonce, laying him out cold.

'Time to go,' I said. Anwer nodded. I picked up a sturdy three-legged stool and hurled it at the window close-by which shattered noisily. At a run, I stepped up on a bench by the wall and dived into the sunlight.

Picture the reaction of the crowd of superstitious villagers who had gathered outside the inn, to the spectacle of a man dressed in the costume of Count Dracula flying through a window towards them. They went bananas. *'Vlad! Vlad! Vlad!'*, they screamed as they fled pell-mell.

A bullet whistled past my head as I scrambled to my feet. I made a dash for the crane, flung myself into the driver's seat and started the motor. Another shot rang out and a bullet struck the steel superstructure, ricocheting into the Dacia and smashing the windscreen. Anwer jumped up beside me, as I strong-armed the gearstick and slammed my foot on the accelerator. We didn't budge, but the lifting arm that had been resting in the flat position reared up behind us and began swinging in an arc, like a windscreen wiper. There were more gunshots, several bullets ringing against the metal of the crane. In desperation, I yanked at another control and found the right one this time. The crane surged forward catching the wing of the Dacia, which crumpled like a soft-drink can.

The crane careered across the square into the narrow

street. There was a loud crash behind us to the left, then another to the right and we juddered and slowed as if being restrained by a powerful friction. Glancing over my shoulder, I saw both sides of the street tumbling in ruins and plumes of dust rising where houses had been. I also saw the raised arm of the crane thrashing right and left, and noticed the chain hanging from the top and the heavy metal ball at the end of it. It was flying through the air left, right, left, right, smashing the old houses to kindling and rubble.

I halted the crane at the top of a small hill, on the edge of the forest. Looking back across the fields, we saw that there wasn't a single house left standing in the village. With some difficulty, I manoeuvred the lifting arm back into the recumbent position and we set off for home base.

'Do you think we should mention this to the Ceausescus when they get back?' I asked as we trundled through the trees. Anwer shook his head, wearing that hang-dog expression I knew so well from our Earls Court flat days.

'Look, we only acted in self-defence,' I said, trying to bolster his spirits. 'They attacked us, remember?'

'Try telling that to the Securitate,' he said morosely. 'They'll have us shot, mark my words.'

It was the same old Anwer. What possessed him to persevere as a pistol-packing minder, was a mystery to me. Temperamentally, he was totally unsuited to the thrills and spills that were part and parcel of the job. More than ever, it was time he made a major career change.

***

The hunt had been a great success. Great white hunter Nicolae Ceausescu had shot two bears, ex-circus beasts I was confidentially informed by one of the beaters, planted there as sacrificial victims, as well as several of the rare and protected Transylvanian black mountain goats. If Gussie and Boy ever

got the hear about what sort of sport he was, he'd be lucky to
avoid a ducking in the Serpentine next time he visited London. Maxwell, who to his credit had little appetite for this sort
of butchery, had bagged a couple of rabbits, while Elena
Ceausescu had winged a beater and seemed very pleased with
her marksmanship. They were all in high spirits and Elena
was even in a generous frame of mind.

'I forgive you everything,' she told Anwer and me when we
greeted them on their return.

'Everything?' he enquired.

'Yes, everything,' said Valentin, translating her words. I
certainly hope so, I thought.

'How did you get on back here? Not too bored, I hope?'
growled Maxwell.

'Oh no,' I replied. 'We had a smashing time.'

★★★

Anwer and I tarried on the wooden balcony while Maxwell
and the Ceausescus went inside for hot baths and their staff
set about their evening duties. Thus we witnessed the ram-
shackle Dacia limp into the clearing. It halted by the crane
and the occupants – the innkeeper and two policemen –
descended and started to inspect it. They were interrupted
by a posse of security guards led by Valentin. Although well
out of earshot, it was plain from the innkeeper's wild arm
movements that he was pretty worked up about something.
About two strangers in a mobile crane playing skittles with
his village, for instance. Realising how unfortunate it would
be if we were recognised, Anwer and I slipped inside and out
of sight.

Dinner was a merry occasion, very different in atmosphere
to the previous evening's repast. The Bulgarian Merlot
flowed freely and the trio at the table were soon behaving as
if they were tipsy, as they were except teetotaller Nicolae.

Maxwell was in his element telling joke after joke, each more obscene than the next. The Ceausescus were in stitches, especially enjoying the one about the parking-warden and the camel, making him repeat him it three times. Frankly, I found their behaviour childish and distasteful, but I was glad enough that they were swapping smut rather than discussing the punishment of the vandals who had demolished a nearby settlement.

After dinner, the merry threesome retired giggling to the sitting room to watch still more episodes of *Kojak*. Maxwell and Elena took seats in front of the super-size television, but Nicolae was led aside by Valentin and they went into a heads-down huddle in a corner of the room. Nicolae nodded earnestly, his countenance growing graver by the second. Crossing the room, he sat down on the sofa next to Elena and, ignoring their guest, had a discussion with her *tête-a-tête*. She looked surprised and raised her hand, signalling to Valentin to join the conversation. After a few words he left the room, returning a minute-or-so later carrying a large sword. All in all, the situation was becoming scary.

'Come over here you two,' instructed Valentin addressing us. We obeyed.

'Kneel,' he said, pointing at a spot in front of Nicolae Ceausescu who was standing brandishing the weapon with both hands. I knelt and closed my eyes. So this was the way they despatched their victims, by impaling them as in days of old. But what about the mess on the carpet? Would house proud Elena stand for it?

Nicolae pronounced some words in Romanian and I felt a tap on the shoulder. I jumped. I opened my eyes and saw the sword descending on Anwer. But instead of cleaving his head from his body, it dubbed him and disappeared from view.

'His excellency President Ceausescu pronounces you members of the Order of Vlad, Second Class without Star, for

services to scientific socialism and the progressive advance-
ment of the Romanian people,' announced Valentin.
Maxwell clapped his hands and gave a loud belch.

'The ceremony may be familiar to you,' said Valentin,
addressing me. 'The President has based it on the customary
procedure in your country when the Queen bestows a knight-
hood. As you know, he received such an honour at Bucking-
ham Palace in 1978.'

I was aware of no such thing, and I wondered what Gussie
and Boy had made of the travesty. The only mercy was that I
hadn't been required to call them Sir Nicolae and Lady Elena
all weekend. They were missing a trick!

I rose slowly and with some difficulty to my feet, my legs
still quivering with fear for my life. The Ceausescus were in
sunny spirits and Maxwell was talking animatedly with
Valentin and laughing heartily.

'What's going on?' I asked him as he gave me a congratu-
latory slap on the back.

'You've done excellently. I'm very pleased,' said the fat
man leading me aside out of Valentin's earshot. He was grinning from chin to chin.

'What?'

'Nicolae and Elena are delighted about your handiwork
with the crane. They think it was my idea and I've allowed
them to go on believing it. No point in letting truth muddy
the water.'

'What are you talking about? I've just flattened a lovely his-
toric hamlet. In England you get put in jail for that sort of
thing.'

'But this is Romania, and here you get a medal. As
Valentin told us in the car, the destruction of the country's
villages and the rehousing of the inhabitants in high rise
apartment blocks is an important part of the modernisation
programme. But much to their frustration it hasn't made

much progress because its very unpopular and people keep sabotaging the equipment. That's why I gave them the crane as a present. They're delighted with the example you've set. So delighted, that my negotiations for cheap newsprint are going to be a piece-of-cake.'

'What about Anwer?' I asked. 'He played a part too.'

'Yes they appreciate that, and as a reward they've decided to make him an ambassador.'

'An ambassador? But he's not Romanian.'

'He is now. They've just awarded him Romanian citizenship.'

'Where is his posting?'

'Back where he comes from. One of the Gulf states, I think.'

Diplomatic life sounded just like Anwer's bowl of cherries. I turned to congratulate him, but Maxwell was already monopolising his attention and I decided against interrupting them. He was on his way home, at last, on an Ambassador Class ticket.

9. *Farewell Robert Maxwell*

To be frank, the end results of my exertions on behalf of Maxwell's *Leaders of the World* series were distinctly disappointing. My biography of Bokassa never saw the light of day. Nor did my dealings with Kim II Sung, Baby Doc Duvalier, Pol Pot, Pablo Escobar or the others, bear fruit as published books, though I could dine out on my adventures. Some titles did appear, notably Ronald Reagan, Leonid Brezhnev, Todor Zhivkov, Erich Honecker and, of course, the Nicolae Ceausescu volume, but I wasn't involved in the production of any of those.

As the years went by, I became more and more convinced that the real purpose of the exercise wasn't the publication of biographies, but to provide Maxwell with a pretext for dropping in on powerful or famous figures around the globe. He craved their company, as others are addicted to drugs or gambling, and if the saints were indisposed he made do with the sinners. In fact, I suspect he felt more at home in their company. I remember his complaints about an invitation to tea with the Pope, because it meant cancelling an appointment with one of the Kray twins. 'Sunshine,' he explained to me, 'Reggie tells much better jokes.'

Maxwell loved being photographed with world-renowned personages. On official trips he always had a professional photographer along to record the occasion, but on our clandestine missions it was your truly who pressed the button. And woe betide me if the results weren't tickety-boo. Just such a GMFU happened with the pictures of our visit to

General Manuel Noriega of Panama, an out-and-out bounder who'd sell his grandmother for the price of a pint. After supper, Noriega took us to see his extensive wall-mounted collection of airline sick bags, a hobby since boyhood. Maxwell suggested a picture of himself and the General shaking hands. Unfortunately I forgot to use the red-eye device and the result looked like a pair of blood-eyed werewolves staring out from a collage of park-a-custard pouches. Maxwell blew a fuse, having intended to send a signed copy to the General who had apparently been very obliging over some financial transactions put through Panamanian banks. He tore a strip off me, using all his usual threats and obscenities, and hurled several volumes of the *Pergamon Encyclopaedia of the German Democratic Republic* at my head. Fortunately he wasn't much of a shot. Then he gave one of his big belly laughs, told a couple of dirty jokes, and we went on as if nothing had happened. That was life with the mercurial Robert Maxwell.

From my point of view, the relationship with Maxwell had many plus points. I enjoyed our jaunts to out of the way places and our meetings with colourful characters. A major benefit of these trips was the passports, identity cards, driving licences and other documents that he provided me with under a variety of aliases. Recognising the necessity of these papers for our future freedom, Jennifer's opposition to my working for him became muted; like a smoking volcano, rather than one spewing rocks and lava.

Getting money out of Maxwell made the proverbial blood-from-a-stone routine seem like child's play. He only paid up when he needed me for another mission, and the cheques were always well short of the full amount. Thus over the years the backlog of money owed grew, especially my unpaid expenses claims. In fact, my bread and butter money came from commissions on selling encyclopaedias up and down the

Costa del Sol, payments he made promptly to encourage me to flog more sets. The precariousness of our household finances meant that Jennifer had to continue her waitressing job in Estepona, which she resented more and more. She held Maxwell directly responsible and added this to her charge sheet of grievances against him. Sometimes I wondered what would happen if she ever met him? It was a prospect that gave me sleepless nights.

Travelling with Maxwell was a trying experience. He was more than just moody, pitching violently from elation to dejection. He could charm the birds out of the trees when it suited him, and then, moments later, be utterly foul-mouthed and foul-tempered for no reason. He seemed actually to enjoy bullying and humiliating his victims. In fact, his behaviour had much in common with the deranged dictators and brigands he sent me to do business with. But at least some of them had decent table manners. Maxwell stuffed his face like a pig and eating with him could be an excruciating experience. I will never forget the occasion in Panama City when the devoured half-a-dozen water melons in as many minutes, spraying the pips over the guard of honour as they performed a march past. Despite the horrors of the *way* he ate, *what* he ate was exquisite and enviable. He travelled with his own supply of Beluga caviar, the finest in the world and Dom Perignon champagne, chilled to perfection, was always on hand. Such nibbles and tipples were some compensation for the ordeal of listening again and again to the same smutty jokes. He told everyone we met the one about the parking warden and the camel, and it hadn't been funny the first time.

As the years went by though, the summonses from Maxwell became less and less frequent. It wasn't difficult to guess why. You just had to buy the *Daily Mirror*, which faithfully reported the antics of its proprietor almost every day, to realise that Maxwell had plenty of other fish to fry and the

Leaders of the World series must have been far from the fore-front of his mind.

Then, in the middle of the furore created by allegations of his involvement with the Israeli secret service I received a call from him. I was to go immediately to Madeira to rendezvous with his yacht. It was the opportunity I had been waiting for the settle my outstanding claims. I drew-up a comprehensive account of the money owed to me, plus compound interest, and it came to a very tidy sum. I would have to choose my moment with care and cunning, but I was determined to confront Maxwell and resolve matters once and for all.

***

Travelling under an assumed identity on one of the false pass-ports supplied by Maxwell, I flew to Madeira. As instructed, I checked into Reid's Hotel, the foremost establishment in the capital, Funchal, and awaited his arrival. I had heard of Reid's, one of the leading grand hotels of the world, but I had never stayed there before. Since Maxwell kept me hanging around for several days before turning-up, I was very glad that he had chosen such an agreeable billet. Established last century, Reid's is a bastion of elegance and refinement. How gratifying, in this day and age, to stay somewhere where the dinner-jacket is *still* the order of the day in the dining room. Actually, this presented me with a bit of a problem since mine was hanging in a cupboard in Marbella. So I went shopping and bought myself a new one, the cost further boosting my expenses claim.

I spent the mornings and afternoons at Reid's lounging by the pool or playing tennis. These pastimes were punctuated by a light buffet lunch on the terrace, and afternoon tea with cucumber sandwiches. What a delight! Evenings began with a vodka martini in the cocktail bar followed by dinner, lamb cutlets, of course, in the hotel's excellent *Les Faunes* restaurant. Afterwards, I repaired to the bar for a glass or two of Ferreira '60 and maybe a turn on the dance floor with one of my acquaintances from the tennis court.

I was bang in the middle of a game of mixed doubles, when Maxwell showed his face. All of a sudden there he was, standing on the terrace, drink in hand, glaring at me. Not wanting to draw too much attention by abandoning the game in mid-match, I decided to wind it up as quickly as possible by muffing my shots. Losing six games in a row when you're already four ahead, requires incompetent play of high order and no amount of 'jolly good shot' could pacify my partner. As she tore a strip off me not only for my shortcomings at tennis but on the dance floor too, I became positively nostalgic for Jennifer. And my humiliation was to no avail, since by the time I stepped off the court Maxwell had gone. But he had left a note instructing me to meet him that evening in the Funchal casino.

★★★

'Madeira's a disaster,' declared Maxwell. 'It's crawling with reptiles.'

We were standing in a cubicle in the gentlemens' lavatory, the usual place for furtive meetings when Maxwell was afraid that he was being followed.

'Snakes?' I enquired, glancing nervously at my feet.

'From the press,' he snapped, jogging my memory that *reptile* was his word for journalists, an unlikely shorthand for a newspaper proprietor. But Maxwell positively detested them, being convinced that they were trying to swindle him by fiddling their expenses.

'A whole horde of reptiles has arrived looking for me. Someone must have tipped them off that I was coming here. I'm leaving immediately.'

An excellent proposal it seemed to me, since Maxwell's

giant girth meant the cubicle was very cramped. But that wasn't what he meant.

'I'm setting sail tonight for Santa Cruz. I'll see you there on Monday evening in the bar at the Hotel Mencey. I want a serious talk with you, but this isn't the time or place.'

'Where's Santa Cruz?' I asked.

'Tenerife. One of the Canary Islands.'

'How do I get there?'

'How the fuck should I know?' he replied in his usual helpful way.

'Can't I come with you on your boat?'

'No way, sunshine. The yacht's staked out by reptiles. I've got enough problems without them spotting Lord Lucan swaggering up the gangplank. I'll get you aboard when I've given them the slip. See you in Santa Cruz. And don't you dare keep me waiting again while you finish a game of tennis. Got it? Now, fuck off.'

I did as I was told. My money would have to wait. There was no mileage in presenting my bill while Maxwell had the mind-set of a Rottweiller.

***

The Hotel Mencey in Santa Cruz, Tenerife, proved to be a charming turn-of-the-century establishment perched at the summit of a steep hill in the centre of town. I sat down in the bar around five o'clock, and had worked my way through half-a-dozen bottles of San Miguel and half a packet of Ducados by the time Maxwell turned up. He was dressed in a beige blazer, checked trousers and a dark blue baseball cap, looking as inconspicuous as an Harrovian at the Fourth of June. I paid my tab, went to the Gents and waited. He joined me a few minutes later. He looked harassed and haggard, as if there were weighty matters on his mind. Now, of course, I know what was troubling him, but then I had no idea.

Maxwell was always doing extraordinary things, and his behaviour, though curious-sounding in retrospect, seemed pretty much par for the course at the time.

As usual he didn't bother with any preliminary civilities, getting straight to the point.

'The yacht's down at the quayside. The name is *Lady Ghislaine*. You can't miss it. It's fucking enormous. Wait till it's dark, then nip up the gang-plank and head for the after-deck. The state-room, my office, leads off the after-deck. I left the doors unlocked. Hide in there till I turn up.'

'Suppose I'm challenged by the crew?'

'Choose a moment when there's nobody about on deck. It'll only take you a few seconds to get aboard. I've sabotaged the video security system, so you won't be spotted by the captain or anyone on the bridge. I'm going to have a meal here and take a drink in a bar. You've got plenty of time to stow-away.'

★★★

Maxwell's plan worked like clockwork and a couple of hours later I was ensconced aboard his gleaming white floating palace. Maxwell himself turned up just after ten o'clock. Locking the steel doors of the state-room behind him, he drew the blinds and turned on the lights.

'I've given the order to set sail,' he said.

'Where are we going?' I asked from an armchair.

'Marbella.'

'That's where I live.'

'Surprise, surprise,' Maxwell replied enigmatically. He sat down opposite me, and changed the subject. 'Listen, sunshine, I'm going to do a Lucan.'

I wasn't sure what he had in mind, but it sounded disagreeable.

'What do you mean? *Do a Lucan?*' I enquired sheepishly.

'Disappear. Like you. And you're going to tell me how its done. So get on with it.'

I was flabbergasted. What on earth did he stand to gain?

'Why?' I exclaimed. 'Why should someone like you, someone who has everything, want to disappear?'

'Oh, personal reasons,' he said sighing wearily. 'I'm tired and I'm fed up. I'm sixty-eight years old and I want out. I want to end my life living quietly in a lovely house with a swimming pool in the middle of nowhere, with no telephones and no worries. Money isn't a problem, I've got plenty of that. I want you to give me the inside track, as a pro, about how to lie low.'

His mention of money reminded me of the expenses claim in my jacket pocket. It seemed like an opportune moment to raise the subject.

'Delighted to be of service,' I said. 'But before we start, I wonder if you could give me a cheque to cover my outstanding expenses. You know Reid's Hotel isn't cheap, and then there's other expenditures I've borne going back years.'

'Sure,' said Maxwell good-naturedly, 'I'll see to it later. Get on with your spiel.' It was the first time I'd ever seen him smile when I raised the subject of money with him. I was very relieved, so relieved that I decided to do as he instructed and collect from him later. I gave him a run-down on my life as a fugitive and revealed the tricks of the trade. Prompted by my reminiscing, Maxwell told me his life story, a decidedly rose-tinted version in the light of subsequent revelations. Fuelled by Dom Perignon and Beluga caviar, we talked on and on into the wee small hours.

***

We are standing at the stern of the boat, basking in a warm, fresh breeze and gazing out over the placid, inky ocean. He glances at his wrist-watch, and I see by the light of the big bright moon that it is 5 am. It will soon be dawn.

'Where the fuck is he?' exclaims Maxwell scanning the horizon.

'Who?'

'Charon,' he replies Delphically. I recognise the name from my schoolboy classical studies as the boatman who ferries people across the Styx, the river separating life and death in Greek mythology. But my erudition leaves me none the wiser.

'When we get to Marbella, what are you going to do?' I ask.

'Go to ground with you. You're the expert.'

I am taken-aback. What will Jennifer say? Moreover, Maxwell is hardly an inconspicuous figure. His presence will endanger all of us.

'How long will you be staying?' I enquire hesitantly.

'Till the heat dies down. Maybe six months.' Six minutes will be too long for Jennifer. But until I've got my money, there is no point in raising objections.

'We must settle my outstanding expenses,' I say handing Maxwell my invoice.

He winces as he takes it from me, holding it between fore-finger and thumb as if touching someone else's snotty hand-kerchief. I realise that his earlier reaction has been simply a ruse to get me to provide him with the benefit of my experience. He is as tight-fisted as ever. Unfolding the piece of paper he peers at it in the moonlight.

'You fucking reptile!' he exclaims, staring at the figures. 'Since when has dinner included the purchase of a dinner jacket?'

His face contorts with rage, or so I think, as he lets the paper slip from his fingers. It flutters to the deck. I stoop to pick it up, then see him clutch at his heart and stagger. I reach out to steady him, but it is too late. He stumbles backwards, trips over the thigh-high thin metal rail and plunges into the briny. My expenses claim is his *coup de grace.*

There it is, the answer to the riddle of Maxwell's death. Of all the absurd conspiracy theories published, none has come close to the truth. That he was laid low by fifteen years' worth of dockets, stubs, receipts and chitties accumulated by Britain's most famous fugitive – Lucky Lucan.

★★★

Watching Maxwell's body float further and further away from the *Lady Ghislane*, it dawned on me that his demise posed a bit of a problem. Sooner or later he would be missed, and in a search for him, I would be discovered. Then, when the body was found, I would be accused of his murder. I considered swimming for it, but since we were in mid-ocean that was tanatamount to suicide. I was in a real pickle.

Just then, the silhouette of a rubber dinghy manned by a single occupant appeared on the horizon. Approaching the stern, the boatman attached a line to the *Lady Ghislane* and hauled himself aboard. As he did so I got a glimpse of his face. It was Anwer.

'What are you doing here?' I spluttered, hardly able to believe my eyes.

'I work for Mr Maxwell,' he replied calmly. 'Mr Maxwell told me all about you. Now I know you're Lucky Lucan, and you're on the run from the police. Everything suddenly makes sense.'

'Why turn up in a dinghy, in the middle of the night?'

'I've come to collect you and Mr Maxwell and take you to the yacht that's sailing to Marbella.'

'That's where the *Lady Ghislaine* is going.'

'Oh no, it's not. The captain has orders to cruise slowly round the Canary Islands, to give us time to get well away.'

'But I thought you'd joined the Romanian diplomatic corps,' I said bewilderdly.

'No fear. I've worked for Mr Maxwell ever since our Romanian investiture. My organisation would never have tolerated me becoming a Romanian ambassador. I'd probably be dead by now. But it was very helpful of him to suggest it to the Ceausescus. It got me out of their clutches. In exchange, I agreed to work for him in a personal capacity. You came to work for him in much the same sort of way, I believe.'

'That's right,' I replied, amazed at these revelations. 'What's your role?'

'I'm his undercover body-guard. I keep an eye out for threats to him and do special jobs. He's got a lot of enemies, you know. I've saved his life on several occasions,' he said proudly.

My brain was working feverishly now. Even though I found it hard to believe that Anwer was anything but half-arsed as a bodyguard, it seemed unlikely that he was going to take the news of his master's demise with equanimity. He'd be after revenge from the supposed killer – me. I had to find a common bond that would over-ride his lust for revenge, and find it quickly. I groped wildly.

'Does Maxwell pay you well?' I asked.

'He hasn't paid me for months,' Anwer replied, 'and sometimes I get pretty pissed off about it. But as you British say, "musn't grumble". Now we ought to get going. It'll be fully light soon. Where is Mr Maxwell?'

'He's dead.'

'Dead?' exclaimed Anwer. 'Who killed him?'

'He died of natural causes. He was very unfit and very over-weight. He had a heart attack and fell into the sea, about ten minutes ago.'

'But he owes me thousands,' said Anwer. My reminder about Maxwell's punctuality of payment had hit home.

Instead of a vengeful bodyguard, I had an ally and a fellow creditor.

'Me too.' I said.

'Let's take a look in the state-room,' said Anwer pensively. 'If he was planning to disappear, he must have put some things aside to take with him. Maybe some money too.'

Anwer led the way to the stateroom and I followed. And there it was, a smart Louis Vuitton overnight bag standing in a corner. Anwer lifted it up on to a table, slipped the latches and raised the lid. It was full of bundles of certificates trussed up with rubber bands.

'Bearer bonds,' breathed Anwer delightedly. 'That's fantastic. Even better than cash. They arouse less suspicion.' His terrorist training had covered more than just bomb-making.

We locked the state-room door to give the impression that Maxwell was asleep inside, and hurried down the deck to the dinghy. Dawn was indeed beginning to break and we were eager to get away before we were spotted.

'How much are the bonds worth?' I asked as I handed the case down to Anwer in the boat.

'Millions, I'm sure. Enough to settle what's owed to us, and the rest can count as our severance payments.'

★★★

'What are you going to do now?' asked Anwer as we bobbed from wave to wave. He had been delighted to let me take the tiller when I told him that I was an experienced powerboat skipper and I'd opened the throttle to get us away from the *Lady Ghislaine* as pronto as possible. I was in my element, my long-dormant love of the sea flooding back to me. Suddenly the future was clear.

'Messing around in boats. That's the life for me,' I replied, shouting to make myself heard above the whistle of the wind and the splash of the spray.

'What?'

'I'm going to buy a big boat with Maxwell's money and sail around the South Seas. A life of sun and sea, and beautiful desert islands with palm trees, long silver beaches and little shacks serving white rum with coconut milk.'

'Like in the Bacardi adverts?'

'Exactly.'

'Sounds very nice,' said Anwer wistfully.

'Why don't you come with us.'

'Us?'

'Me and Jennifer. You met her in Earls Court. We could use another member of crew.'

'She won't want me along.'

'Of course she will. She'll be delighted.'

In fact, Anwer was much nearer the truth, but I knew she would see the sense of having him, the only person who possessed the secret of my identity, safely in sight, at least until the hue and cry following Maxwell's death died down. The fat man had been right. I did know a trick or two about survival as a fugitive. Besides, Jennifer, with her county upbringing would appreciate someone else to cook and clean for us.

'Very well. I accept,' said Anwer after only a few seconds reflection.

'Bora-Bora or bust!' I yelled as I gunned the outboard and we sped towards tropical paradise.

10. *Desert Island Diversions*

Jennifer was cock-a-hoop at the idea of uppinging sticks and sailing the ocean blue. She even accepted that Anwer was coming with us without demur, after enquiring about his knot-tying, mop pushing and saucepan wielding abilities. Plainly she saw his role as a deck-hand cum galley-slave, which was distinctly bad news, food wise. In fact, I had my own rather more ambitious career plan for Anwer, but it wasn't wholly incompatible with Jennifer's.

The expose of Maxwell's frauds in the months following his death made fascinating reading. Jennifer took a particularly close interest. Every new revelation was greeted with a 'tut-tut' or a 'what did I tell you?' As the scandal unfolded, we made preparations for our new life. I busied myself brushing-up on sailing and navigation, while Jennifer organised the conversion of our cache of bearer bonds into convenient off-shore bank account balances, and read everything she could get her hands on about the South Seas. She also arranged for Anwer to work as a *sous-chef* in the restaurant in Estepona to learn the rudiments of cookery.

A few months later, with our tracks in Marbella well disguised, my maritime skills up to speed, Jennifer possessed of all the knowledge books could teach about the New Hebrides, the Solomon Islands, New Caledonia, Fiji, Tonga, and Samoa, and Anwer having mastered boiling an egg, we set off. In New Zealand, with funds furnished by Maxwell's bearer bonds, we bought a magnificent ocean-going boat that we kitted out for every conceivable contingency or whim.

Nevertheless, somehow writing paper got overlooked, so I scribbled these memoirs on the Bronco bog paper that Jennifer had bought for Anwer's loo. Pointing the prow towards the thousands of square miles of tropical Pacific Ocean, we weighed anchor.

Not for one moment have I regretted the decision to leave so-called 'civilisation' behind, and I'm sure I speak for Jennifer and Anwer. The weather's all sunshine and warm sea breezes. There's no traffic, no fumes, no bustle, and no man-made eyesores, just the serenity of the lapping of the waves and the sparkling sea stretching to the horizon where it meets the clear blue sky. And no rat-race. The commuters here are playful porpoises, flashing flying-fish and sometimes a great white Albatross floating astern. What could be more idyllic?

Above all, there's *time*. Time to think. Time to read. Time to write. Time to talk. We listen a lot to the BBC World Service, a habit picked up in the Falklands. I must say that it gives me great pleasure to discuss the questions of the day with Jennifer and Anwer, and to set them straight on moral dilemmas and political issues. Our discussions are always fruitful and one-sided.

And time, too, to play. One of our parlour games is inspired by the popular BBC programme Desert Island Discs. Sometimes we vary the format – Desert Island Dress Designers for Jennifer, or Desert Island Detonators for Anwer – but it's the musical version I like. Selecting the eight records I would have with me on the island, whittling them down to one, plus book and object of no practical use. It is the perfect pastime for lounging around on deserted ribbons of silver sand, caressed by a gentle surf and flanked by tall coconut palms, their fronds shimmering sensuously in the breeze.

★★★

I vividly recall one such occasion on the New Hebrides island of Motalava, which is just the sort of place Roy Plumley must have had in mind. We were lying on the sun-warmed sand of the beach, the air feathery as it stroked our faces, waiting for the sun to dip below the yard-arm, so to speak, looking forward to our first thirst-quencher; it was my turn to play guest, Jennifer's to play host.

Jennifer: My castaway today is Britain's most famous fugitive. He is Lucky Lucan.

Lucky: Hello, licence-holders.

Jennifer: Lucky, as a fugitive, you must be no stranger to solitude.

Lucky: Far from it, old sausage. Never met so many people in my life, since I've been on the run.

Jennifer: Let me put the question another way, how do you think you could cope on your own on a desert island?

Lucky: By myself? What about you and Anwer?

Jennifer: We won't be there. It's against the rules.

Lucky: Don't be ridiculous. You *are* here.

Jennifer: Not here. There!

Lucky: Where?

Jennifer: Oh, never mind. Tell me, could you fend for yourself? Make a shelter and a fire, for instance.

Lucky: I wouldn't like to poke my nose in. My butler deals with that sort of thing.

Jennifer: No, no. I've already told you, that's against the rules.

Lucky: You'll have to change the rules, old sausage. He's very touchy about his domain. Aren't you Anwer?

Jennifer: (exasperated) Quiet, Anwer. Let's have your first record.

Lucky: *A Nightingale Sang In Berkeley Square*. The Clermont Club, my old stomping ground, is in Berkeley Square. Many are the hours I've spent gazing out of the window at the

Square while Squiffy told one of his interminable anecdotes. From upstairs at the Club, it looks like a glorified traffic island. But at least it's grassy, which is probably why the nightingale decided to sing there rather than in Sloane Square. Now Belgrave Square. . .

Jennifer: That's enough squares. Why that record?

Lucky: I've heard many versions of this charming song, but to my mind the most original interpretation is by Barbara Cartland on her disc *Barbara Cartland's Album of Love Songs Sung Especially For You* backed by the Royal Philharmonic Orchestra and the Mike Sammes Singers. I have to admit that I'm not a great fan of her books, but as a singer she's, well, unforgettable.

Jennifer: She's also Princess Diana's step-grandmother.

Lucky: Which brings us to my next record, which also has royal family connections. It's performed by Princess Margaret's friend Roddy Llewellyn. He's also an accomplished landscape gardener. A sort of latter-day Renaissance man, one might say.

Jennifer: What's the song?

Lucky: *Crazy World,* from the album *Roddy*.

Jennifer: He's singing flat.

Lucky: No, no, he's emotionally overwrought. That's pain in his voice. Listen to the words: 'What's is all about?. . . 'Cos it's a crazy world to me'. I know why he sounds kind of, well, anguished. I've been there too.

Jennifer: Still sounds flat to me. Record number three?

Lucky: *Je T'aime Moi Non Plus*, sung, if that's the *mot juste*, by Serge Gainsbourg and Jane Birkin. Your favourite, old sausage, and a record that always reminds me of you.

Jennifer: Thank you, sweetie.

Lucky: Frankly, I've never been able to fathom the meaning of the title, let alone get to grips with the rest of what's going on. It's called *Love At First Sight* on the album

Hawaiian Honeymoon by Basil Henriques and the Waikiki Islanders, which strikes me as taking more than a couple of liberties with the translation. Then there's the version by Frankie Howerd and June Whitfield. Until I heard their English language interpretation, I'd never realised that the lyrics were about a game of golf.

Jennifer: What's the next record?

Lucky: *Mystery Train*. Elvis Presley, of course, on the LP entitled *The Complete Sun Sessions*. Before my encounter with Elvis I was a bit of a stuffed shirt about pop music. I'm eternally grateful to him for opening my ears. That evening at Graceland when I played the bongos with him, was the turning point.

***

Jennifer: Record number five?

Lucky: *Flick of the Wrist*, by Queen from the album *Sheer Heart Attack*. Kills two birds with one stone, this one. It reminds me of the time in the flat at Earls Court when we were plotting the assassination of Harold Wilson and Anwer was driving me up the wall with his Queen and Bay City Rollers records. Also the wild-goose-chase Robert Maxwell sent me on in the island of Ibiza.

Jennifer (surprised): You've never mentioned that before.

Lucky: You were visiting your mother at the time. You always made such a song and dance about me working for Maxwell, I thought it best to keep quiet about the episode.

Jennifer: What happened?

Lucky: I was in the bath when Maxwell called, so it took me a couple of minutes to get to the 'phone. He blasted my ears for keeping him waiting and ordered me to go immediately to Pike's Hotel in Ibiza. He told me that he'd had a tip-off about a convention of London merchant bankers. I was to use any means, fair or foul, to discover what they were up to and get some pictures.

I was a tad vexed, because I wanted to watch the big power-boat race on TV that afternoon, so I told him that I wasn't feeling quite 20 shillings to the pound. I should have known better.

'Listen, sunshine, and listen good,' he yelled down the blower. 'Either you get your arse to fucking Ibiza or tomorrow's headline in the *Daily Mirror* will read LUCAN FOUND IN MARBELLA HIDEAWAY. Got that?'

So off I went to do his bidding, but my heart wasn't in it. Oh, it wasn't the cloak and dagger dimension. I'd become used to that. But I was fed up with nights alone in hotels in far flung places. Maybe one day I'll write *Lucky Lucan's Lonely Hotel Guide* based on my experiences.

Maxwell was decidedly short on detail about the gathering, but I had the impression that it had something to do with Warburgs. Having myself worked briefly as a City merchant banker, I knew the tribe and spoke their lingo and was fully aware of Warburg's formidable reputation. I also knew that over the years Maxwell had had a number of run-ins with them, when they were acting for the other side in deals he was doing. In fact they were *always* acting for the other side, because they wouldn't touch such a dubious character with a barge-pole. Maxwell greatly resented their attitude, so it made some sense that he should send to me spy on people he regarded as adversaries. On the other hand, Ibiza, revelling in a reputation for hedonism and *louche* behaviour, seemed a decidedly improbable venue for a meeting of ultra-respectable merchant bankers.

It had become dark by the time I reached Pike's Hotel, a large old farm house with extensive grounds expensively converted into a top-class establishment. The scene that greeted me was far from what I had expected. The place was festooned with brightly coloured paper streamers and an enormous *al fresco* party was in full swing with a cast of hundreds. The guests were whooping it up like troupe of baboons. If this was Warburgs letting its hair down, Maxwell, and the world, would be interested. I spotted a photographer taking party snaps and eventually negotiated a duplicate set of prints. But the price he demanded was outrageous; far more than I was prepared to pay without Maxwell's say-so. So I went inside the hotel and found a 'phone, expecting that my revelations would put him good humour.

'Sorry to trouble you, Mr Maxwell. I'm at the conference in Ibiza. There's a wild party going on. I've arranged for a set of photographs, but. . .'

'Shut up, sunshine,' said Maxwell interrupting. 'Forget about it. Go home.' The line went dead. Even in those few words, I'd detected an uncharacteristically crestfallen tone of voice. Something was wrong.

I wandered outside into the courtyard where the revelries were in full flight. My clandestine mission cancelled, I felt awkward and unwelcome. I didn't just feel like a gatecrasher, I looked like one. Expecting a gathering of bankers I was respectably dressed in a navy blazer, grey flannels and silk cravat, but everyone else was outrageously attired and some of the women were wearing almost nothing at all.

'Having a good time?' said an English voice. I looked round. The speaker was a slight, dapper, dark-haired man in his thirties, with a long face with alert eyes and a puckish smile.

'Yes, thank you,' I said, lying. I felt ill-at-ease and mighty confused. The revellers were not behaving at all like serious-minded, sober-mannered merchant bankers.

'I'm Freddie,' announced the stranger.

'Err, John,' I replied, hoping that was the name in the passport I was travelling on.

'Have a drink, John,' said Freddie.

He nodded towards me and a waiter appeared at my side carrying a tray of glasses of champagne. I drew the conclusion that he must be a senior executive of the firm, though he was the rummest looking merchant banker I'd ever set eyes on.

'Err, what side of the business are you on?' I enquired, trying to make conversation.

He looked puzzled.

'I'm the singer,' he replied.

Blimey, I thought, merchant banking has certainly changed since my days in the City. Feeling a bit stumped for an appropriate response, I asked the obvious question.

'Would that be corporate finance or investment management?'

'That's one of my records playing now,' he replied.

I listened. There was something haunting about the song. And then I realised where I'd heard it before – it was another of the records played by Anwer in the flat in Earls Court. I racked my mind to recall the music he had tortured me with all those years ago. And then it came to me.

'You must be the Bay City Rollers,' I blurted.

'We bloody well are not. I'm Freddie Mercury and the band's called Queen.' He sounded distinctly miffed.

'Mercury?' I mused, turning the word over in my mind.

'That's right. And this is my birthday party?'

In a flash, Maxwell's muddle became clear. Mercury was the singer's name, but it was also the name of the company that owned Warburgs. Somehow Maxwell, or his informant, had confused Freddie Mercury and Mercury International. This was no gathering of bankers, it was a pop star's bacchanalia. No wonder Maxwell had sounded so down-in-the-mouth on the 'phone. It was a ludicrous mistake. I burst into laughter. I roared and guffawed until tears filled my eyes.

'What's so funny?' asked Freddie, who was plainly not amused. 'Who are you? What are you doing at my party?'

'Robert Maxwell sent me. . .' I spluttered, still chortling. I didn't have time to say any more. At a flick of the wrist from my host, a brace of bodyguards grabbed my arms, carried me over to the swimming pool and threw me in. That was Freddie Mercury's verdict on the tabloid press.

After my ducking, Freddie was very hospitable. Somebody produced some dry clothes of a bizarrely Bohemian sort, and I felt much less self-conscious blending with the revellers. In fact, I boogie-woogied into the wee hours and thoroughly enjoyed myself.

Jennifer: So you went dancing while I was at my mother? I'm not surprised you kept quiet about it. What else did you get up to while I was away?

Lucky: Let's move on to my next record. *Jealousy*, the most famous of all tango tunes. This is to remind me of the Falklands under Argentine occupation and that dirty rat Enrico who was trying to get his paws on you. . .

Jennifer: That's quite enough of that sort of talk in front of Anwer. Record number seven?

Lucky: *My Way*, by Frank Sinatra. 'You'll do it *my way*', was one of Robert Maxwell's well-worn phrases. It was usually the prelude to despatching me to pow-wow with yet another beastly Third World dictator. I want it to remind me that I'm no longer beholden to him or anyone else.

As tunes go it's a hummable one, and I've often warbled through it in the shower in the morning. It's also the only song I've ever performed in public.

Jennifer: (puzzled) When did you do that?

Lucky: Whoops. Another confession. Remember the evening we moored in Malekula? You and Anwer were pooped and hit the hay, but I was full of beans. So I took a stroll alone along the quayside and popped into the Kakamora Bar, for a night-cap. But a tourist tour-bus had got there first and the place was full of Santory-swigging

Japanese. They were having a jolly singalong with a cunning contraption called a karaoke machine. I'd never seen one before. After a few vodka martinis I got caught up in the *bonhomie* of the occasion and allowed my new Japanese friends to persuade me to have a go. Given a choice between *My Way* and *Yellow Submarine*, I plumped for the former. My rendition was received with respectful good manners by the Japanese – once I'd finished they just sat there in total silence.

***

Jennifer: We'll move on smartly to your last record.

Lucky: *Albatross*, performed by Basil Henriques and the Waikiki Islanders on the album *Hawaiian Honeymoon*. The sideways sound of the Hawaiian harp is the perfect musical accompaniment to a glorious South Seas sunset, bathing a desert island in its warm glow. Speaking of which, where's Anwer? It's sundowner time.

Jennifer: If you could take only one record, which would it be?

Lucky: It would be *The Lambada*. It's the nearest thing to a song with lamb cutlets in the title.

Jennifer: No, no. That's cheating. It's not one of the eight.

Lucky: Oh alright. Anwer can bring it as one of his choices.

Jennifer: What about a book? Remember that the Bible and Shakespeare are already there.

Lucky: I'll take *Your Round, Jeeves*, by P. G. Woodhouse. I've always enjoyed the Bertie Wooster stories, which never fail to amuse, however many times one thumbs the pages. And instructional too for Anwer. What better role model could he have than Jeeves? Now where are those drinks?

Jennifer: Hold on. We haven't finished yet. What about the object of no practical use?

Lucky: That has to be the Clermont Club, with Squiffy,

Gussie and Boy in attendance.

Jennifer: You're taking liberties again. You're not allowed to take friends with you.

Lucky: Oh come off it, old sausage, you said I couldn't take objects of practical use. What on earth practical use could there be for Squiffy, Gussie and Boy?

***

Night falls quickly in the tropics after the sun slips below the horizon. Now the clear sky is inky blue-black, flecked with millions of twinkling stars.

Anwer arrives with my vodka martini. He places it by my elbow.

'Will you be dressing for dinner tonight?' he enquires.

'What's on the menu?'

'Tonight, it's lamb cutlets *en gelée*.'

'In that case, we certainly will.'

'Very good, your lordship. I'll lay out your clothes in your cabin. Will that be all?'

'Yes. Thank you. Anwer.'

***

I gaze up at the big bright moon, floating before my eyes like a hypnotist's pendulum. I study the markings on its surface, trying to make my own sense of one of the mysteries man has pondered through the ages. Out of the shadows and shapes a pattern emerges. Then, like a film, it switches from half-tone to colour, and before me in all its glory is the Clermont Club.

The big panelled front door swings open. I enter the magnificent cream and gilt Adam hall. I ascend one of the twin staircases that bow upwards to the gaming rooms. Gussie and Boy are sitting at the green baize table, surrounded by the familiar backdrop of sherbet-tinted walls, hung with Georgian portraits, and pine-coloured drapes. Squiffy is there too, in a corner clutching a brandy balloon, telling a story to some poor blighter. There's a comforting buzz of conversation, the chink of glasses, the aroma of cigars, and the distant rattle of plates and cutlery from the dining room. I'm suffused by a warm glow, as though I've just scoffed a rack of cutlets and quaffed a bottle of *Chateau Petrus* '61. When I fall at the final fence, this celestial Clermont Club is the heaven I'd like to be my resting place.

The vision fades and I'm back to here and now; a beach in the South Seas with Jennifer and my gentleman's gentleman. A little bit of heaven on earth.

***

There's a tune playing in my head. It's that old song about the nightingale in Berkeley Square.

'May I have the pleasure of the next dance?' I enquire.

'How delightful that would be,' Jennifer replies.

We rise to our feet, slip arms around each other and trip the light fantastic. As we spin like dervishes, the last verse of a rhyme I learnt in childhood comes to mind:

> *And hand in hand, on the edge of the sand,*
> *They danced by the light of the moon,*
> *The moon,*
> *The moon,*
> *They danced by the light of the moon.*

Editor's Afterword

My first and only meeting with Lord 'Lucky' Lucan was as extraordinary as any of the episodes he recounts in his remarkable memoirs.

It was on the island of Matareva, which I visited while writing an article following the footsteps of Paul Gaugin around Polynesia. One evening, as I sat on the veranda of my room in the Hotel du Port, sipping a Dubonnet fizz and watching the tropical sunset, there was a knock at the door. The caller was a tall, tanned, distinguished-looking Englishman. A stranger, but somehow familiar. He introduced himself simply as 'Lucky'.

'Sorry to trouble you, old chap, but the word in the bar downstairs is that you're a writer,' he said, stepping across the threshold.

'I do freelance travel journalism,' I replied.

'Know anyone in publishing?'

'I have a friend who is an editor.'

'That'll do. Look, I've written my memoirs and I want to get them into print. I'd be grateful if you'd pass them on to your chum.'

'Alright,' I said, too taken aback with surprise to turn down his request. 'But I ought to warn you that they're pretty fussy about what they publish.'

'Judge for yourself,' he said. He opened his large black leather brief-case and pulled out a thick sheaf of coarse crackly paper, covered in neat scribblings in blue biro.

'Sorry about the bog-paper, old boy. We're right out of

Basildon Bond.' He sat down in a cane armchair, placed his
Panama hat on his lap and leaned back reposefully.

He clearly had no intention of leaving until I'd looked at his
stuff, so I took a chair and began to read.

Mercifully, I have never been struck by lightning, but I
imagine that the experience is not dissimilar to what I felt at
the moment when, all of a sudden, I realised that the author
was Lucan. Any doubts about his identity were dispelled by
his appearance. He looked as he did in the photos that had
appeared in the press years ago, moustache and all.

He smiled and nodded, confirming my conclusion.

'What do you think of my scribblings?' he said in an
amiable voice.

'I think they provide the answer to some of the greatest
riddles of recent times.'

'Just thought I'd set the record straight. Do you think your
friend will be interested?'

'He'd be crazy not to be. Mind you, they need polishing in
places to smooth down the rough edges.'

'Oh dear,' he said sounding somewhat crestfallen. 'It's my
first attempt as a writer. Look here, would you be prepared to
help me? I would be really grateful.'

'Me?'

'There isn't anyone else I can ask,' he replied glumly.

'I would be delighted,' I heard myself saying, wondering
what I was doing.

'Excellent,' he said, brightening. 'I'm going to leave it up
to you to do whatever's necessary to get it into the station
bookstalls. Do you think the publisher will want pictures?'

'I don't know?'

'Well have these, just in case,' he said dipping his hand into
the brief-case and pulling out an envelope stuffed of photographs. 'They're snaps that I've collected over the years. I've
written what they are on the back.'

He looked at his watch and frowned.

'So much to do, so little time,' he muttered to himself. Then, addressing me, he said, 'I'm afraid I must get back to the boat. We sail almost immediately.'

'But how will I let you know what happens?'

'Oh, I'll pick up a copy somewhere. You and I will never meet again. Don't try looking for me. I've had plenty of practice at disappearing. It's your show now.'

He rose and made his way to the door. We shook hands. And he was gone.

★★★

I have checked dates and details about the people, places and events he mentions, where these can be verified by information in the public domain, and can testify that the framework of facts is historically accurate. But I can find no trace of any living person who bears a resemblance to Jennifer or Anwer, not to mention Squiffy Marchmain, Gussie and Boy. Plainly these are *noms de plume* to protect the identities of friends and acquaintances.

I have edited his text lightly, retaining his choice of word or turn of phrase as much as possible. His is a unique authorial voice.

I hope he approves, wherever he may be.

HUMOUR TITLES

☐	1 85283 787 X	Absolutely: The Words	£6.99 pb
☐	0 7522 0500 5	Animal Lovers	£4.99 pb
☐	0 7522 1617 1	Another Pair of Underpants	£4.99 pb
☐	0 7522 0678 8	Baldyman: Creating An Impression	£7.99 pb
☐	0 7522 0943 4	Beavis and Butthead: This Book Sucks	£6.99 pb
☐	0 7522 0854 3	Dilbert: Always Postpone Meetings with Time Wasting Morons	£4.99 pb
☐	0 7522 0136 0	Dilbert: Bring Me the Head of Willy the Mail Boy	£4.99 pb
☐	0 7522 0849 7	Dilbert: Shave the Wales	£4.99 pb
☐	0 7522 0632 X	Eurotrash: A Weird Guide to Europe	£10.99 pb
☐	0 7522 0832 2	Fleas, Knees and Hidden Elephants	£6.99 hb
☐	0 7522 0157 3	Fleas, Knees and Hidden Elephants	£4.99 pb
☐	0 7522 0615 X	Foxtrot – Foxtrot	£4.99 pb
☐	0 7522 0620 6	Foxtrot – Pass the Loot	£4.99 pb
☐	0 7522 0896 9	Gordon Brittas: Sharing the Dream	£6.99 pb
☐	1 85283 768 3	Mr Bean's Diary	£6.99 hb
☐	1 85283 349 1	Mr Bean's Diary	£4.99 pb
☐	0 7522 0994 9	Mr Bean's Mini Diary	£3.99 pb
☐	0 7522 0775 X	Paul Merton: My Struggle	£7.99 hb
☐	0 7522 0761 X	Roy Chubby Brown Unzipped	£6.99 pb
☐	0 7522 0182 4	A Woman's Little Instruction Book	£3.99 pb

All these books are available at your local bookshop or can be ordered direct from the publisher. Just tick the titles you want and fill in the form below.

Prices and availability subject to change without notice.

Boxtree Cash Sales, P.O. Box 11, Falmouth, Cornwall TR10 9EN

Please send a cheque or postal order for the value of the book and add the following for postage and packing:

U.K. including B.F.P.O. – £1.00 for one book plus 50p for the second book, and 30p for each additional book ordered up to a £3.00 maximum.

Overseas including Eire – £2.00 for the first book plus £1.00 for the second book, and 50p for each additional book ordered.

OR please debit this amount from my Access/Visa Card (delete as appropriate).

Card Number ☐☐☐☐☐☐☐☐☐☐☐☐☐☐☐☐

Amount £ ....

Expiry Date ....

Signed ....

Name ....

Address ....

PAUL MERTON –
MY STRUGGLE

Paul Merton

★ Paul Merton who presents *My Struggle* is essentially a fictional character, writing about Growing Up in the East End, The Last Days of The Music Halls, My Influences, Pinewood, Success in the Sixties, The Hard Times, The Depression, The Wives . . . the list is endless

★ A clever take off of the show-biz autobiography genre

★ Contains photographs of Paul Merton in his spoof character, the popular entertainer whose hilarious tale captivates the reader

★ The lucky reader will discover a cunningly integrated book, with spoof archive pictures, 'mementos' and visual gags galore . . .

Paul Merton – My Struggle is available from
Boxtree and all good bookshops priced £7.99 hb
(0 7522 0775 X)

THE BALDY MAN – CREATING AN IMPRESSION

Colin Gilbert & Niall Clark

* Humour in the tradition of Mr Bean

* Will be shown on television throughout the year

* Hilarious TV show starring Gregor Fisher also known as Rab C Nesbitt

* Baldyman's guide for the reader on how to "make an impression" in modern life

* Unaware of his vanity, bad taste, personal hang-ups and bizarre psychoses, The Baldy Man opens up to the reader giving us what he considers to be honest, good and invaluable advice

* Combined with great photos, capturing all of Gregor's facial grimacing from smug, self satisfied preening to mocking disdain, *Creating An Impression* is set to have the nation rollicking with laughter at The Baldy Man's attempts to be stylish, trendy and cool!

The Baldy Man – Creating An Impression is available from all good bookshops and direct from Boxtree
0 7522 0678 8 – priced £7.99 pb